Tabula Rasa

BEYOND A PLACE CALLED THERE . . .

May the blessings of [illegible] surround you and bring you joy!

Zoltan Powell

IMPORTANT AUTHOR'S NOTE

In an effort to share the truth and my personal experiences, some of the situations depicted herein may be too graphic for younger readers. Parental discretion is advised.

Tabula Rasa / Zoltan Powell —1st ed.
ISBN 978-0-578-58782-0

Tabula Rasa: An opportunity to start over without prejudice in having a “Clean Slate”

FROM THE AUTHOR:

This book is based on a true story. *My* true story.

However, some of the names have been changed in order to protect the identity and safety of those who were and are involved.

I refer to those who were residents with me at the orphanage as my siblings. At this time, I have no way of knowing if there were or are any blood relatives of mine alive today. Perhaps that will be another story for another time.

For now, this is my story, as I remember it.

Zoltan Powell
Author

ACKNOWLEDGMENTS

To Kevin Anderson and Associates: Thank you for reviewing my first rough draft manuscript and believing in my work.

To Whitney Soderberg: Thanks for being patient and helping me with my photo shoot. I am utterly grateful; without you I would not look so good.

To Sean Khamphouang: Thank you so much for giving me your keen insight and helping me with the front part of the book cover.

To Daniel Forrest: Without your awesome art talent I would not have been able to design my own book cover. I am truly grateful for your encouragement and commitment.

To Pam Nolde: Thank you for taking my manuscript and helping me fine-tune the details. Because of your efforts, this book came alive, and I am very grateful for the wisdom you have shared.

To Marilyn Jackson: Many thanks for your contribution of detail suggestions within the manuscript. You have been a blessing in helping me complete this work and convey my story.

To All My Dear Friends: I would love to name every single one of you. Time and space and ink and paper prevent it. There are way more of you than I can name. *You know who you are.* Thank you so much for being patient with me and believing in me through my growth. Without your encouragements this book would have never been possible, and my life would be much different from what it is.

DEDICATION

I dedicate this book to all of the parents who have adopted both United States and foreign orphans. It is dedicated as well to each and every orphan who hopes for a home.

Adoption brings a blending of lives that is nothing less than grace. The wealth of knowledge and love put forth is miraculous in itself. I hope each of you will walk boldly into a future filled with limitless opportunities and grow along the journey.

PREFACE

Nicolae Ceausescu was the second (and last) communist leader of Romania. He ruled as the nation's general secretary from 1965 to 1989.

During his tenure, in 1966, he ordered a proclamation known as Decree 770. This decree enacted a law intended to reverse the low fertility rate. This, Ceausescu hoped, would increase the country's population and help the state achieve autonomy. Under the law, contraceptives such as birth control pills disappeared from the shelves of all drugstores, and all women were forced to be monitored monthly by a gynecologist. There were only two ways in which this decree would not apply: if a woman were forty-five years of age or older, and if a woman of any age had at least four children in her care.

Any pregnancies detected were to be monitored through birth by private police officers who oversaw the hospitals. In order to encourage new births, mothers who had children as recommended were granted significant benefits to help with the household income. If a mother had at least ten children, the Romanian state would declare her a Heroine Mother.

Due to Decree 770, the number of births in Romania skyrocketed, resulting in many children being abandoned by their families and put into orphanages, where they were subjected to institutionalized neglect, as well as physical and sexual abuse. In 1990, international journalists were permitted into Romania, revealing crammed institutions rife with appalling conditions. Overall, it is estimated about 500,000 children were raised in communist orphanages.

I am one of those many children. This is my story.

CHAPTER ONE

It was early morning in Targu, Mures Romania. I lay in the cozy, warm bed, drifting in and out of sleep as fresh, cold air blew in from the window. *I am in heaven and at peace,* I thought as I covered my head to keep warm and slowly drifted back to sleep.

Suddenly, a sharp pain shot through my feet. I quickly tried to pull my legs back toward my body. The pain intensified regardless of how much I struggled to get free. Everything was pitch black around me. I could smell the aroma of musky urine, intensifying with every breath I took as I kicked and jerked my feet in hopes of escaping this bad dream. However, no matter what I tried to do, I could not muster the strength to get away from that which had a hold of me.

I soon gave up in pure exhaustion. I lay there, the pain in my feet intensifying without mercy. When I submitted, my feet were released. Tears rolled down my cheeks as I lay there, trying to escape the horrible dream. Light pierced my eyes as the blanket was yanked off of me. The torturous pain from the base of my feet synchronized to the rhythm of my heart.

I rubbed my eyes. Once my vision adjusted to the dim light seeping in through the edges of the window, I saw in front of me a short, stocky man wearing a dirty blue shirt. He wore oversized denim overalls and held a stick in his hand. His skin color was a light brown; his hair was short, curly, and black. A dark, untamed beard hid some of his facial features. I gazed into his little, brown pebble eyes in hopes of discovering some form of grace. I found none. He grabbed me by my feet once more, yanking me straight onto the scratched, unpolished, dark wooden floor. The terror I hoped was ending was instead just beginning.

CHAPTER TWO

The male staff member looked at me without remorse. Finished with me, he took off to devour his next prey. I heard the cries intensify around me. I propped myself up, wiping away my tears, knowing I needed to get up. I lifted my left foot first, putting just some of my weight on it. The pain intensified with every ounce of pressure. Nonetheless, I bit my lip, put pressure on my right foot, and let out a small whimper as I held on to the edge of my bed to maintain my balance. I looked around, trying to ignore the pain as everything within my consciousness started to flood back.

I gazed around at what I called my home. The white, creamy-textured walls had holes scattered across them, the result of years of previous "accidents" like an angry fist through the wall or a child's head banged against it. Along the floorboards were kick marks to match. Multiple light-brown wooden beds were crammed next to each other. There were scratch and bite marks carved into their frames. My siblings lay in these beds, awash in their own urine and feces. Cold air blew in through the window across from me. It was still more dark than light outside, so the only thing I could see clearly were the dark, forest-green bars on the windows, designed to keep us in.

Next to the window was a fireplace, and to my left and right were doors that led to adjoining rooms, similar to the one in which I was standing. Suddenly, out the corner of my eye, I saw a young female staff member in her late twenties come through the doorway behind me. She was carrying a big white sheet over her shoulder. A couple of other chaperones followed her, also carrying sheets, heading toward the other rooms. The one who came into our room was thin, and wore an old, white uniform almost completely worn out. Dark brown hair draped a little past her shoulder. Her stern expression never changed as she made her way to the middle of the room and plopped the big white sheet on the dark, wooden floor.

I watched her intently while she quickly undid the sheet, revealing a pile of clothes. Once the bag was undone, she stood back and nodded, giving us permission to move toward it. My siblings rushed to the middle of the pile, grabbing and grappling with each other, picking up anything and everything that looked as if it might fit them.

I watched in amazement, slowly but surely making my way to the center of the room. I sat down in front of the pile to give my feet some rest. While I dug through the pile of clothes, I could still hear the cries of my siblings echoing around me from the other rooms. Still the stink of urine and feces filled my nostrils, intermixing with the fresh, cold air coming in from outside.

I rummaged through the clothes, trying to find something that would fit. I grabbed the best next thing I could get my hands on and slowly made my way back toward my bed. I put on a pair of pink and white flower-patterned pants, followed by a gold turtleneck. I'm sure the outfit was not one I would have chosen had there been anything else that might have fit me. However, in these circumstances, I had already learned to take what was given without complaint.

I had been given a pair of shoes. The only problem was, it was not actually a "pair" it was just two left shoes, probably not even the same size and definitely not the same style. While I reached down to put my two left shoes on my feet, the stocky male chaperone with overalls made his way back to the center of the bedrooms, yelling, "Line up!". I got up as fast as I could and made my way into formation.

Once everyone was in line, we were corralled forward. As I started walking, the pain in the soles of my feet became even stronger. The left shoe on my right foot rubbed awkwardly against the back of my heel. Nonetheless, I tried to block out the pain. I looked down at the red-and-white-patterned carpet, held in place by the brass crossbars at the back of each step. With every step, I could only hope I would not stumble or fall. I listened to the metal rods colliding within the inserts as we marched toward the cafeteria.

CHAPTER THREE

My stomach grumbled as I followed my siblings down the long, cold hallway that led to the cafeteria. Windows ran along the hallway on my left. The smell of fresh bread filled my lungs as I shuffled down the line, anticipating a good breakfast. Once we all arrived inside, a staff member commanded us to stay in line and make our way toward the kitchen window.

The cafeteria was bare, without chairs or tables. While I shuffled ahead I noticed a small, frail boy with a dark complexion sitting on the floor, making strange noises. He had on a white, long-sleeved shirt with some bright yellow shorts he had already soiled. He sat there chewing on the right-hand sleeve of his shirt, looking around with brown, innocent eyes and rocking back and forth, seemingly with no perception of the reality in which he lived. I brought my attention back to the line, gently putting my hands out in front of me without making eye contact, and making my way to the window.

Once I had the bread and cup of water in my hand, I walked away and found a place near the big fireplace, away from everyone else. Once I felt secure, I took a seat and dipped my bread in the rusty cup of water to soften the staleness. Within seconds I'd devoured the bread and drank the remaining water, tasting the bread particles that floated within. Once every drop of water was gone, I set my cup down and awaited the staff's next command.

I was sitting there quietly, listening to my siblings smack their mouths as they finished their own breakfasts. Suddenly a loud cry erupted, overpowering all the other sounds around me. I closed my eyes in fear of what was happening, fear of seeing something I was not intended to see. I instinctively tilted my head down to avoid punishment.

I felt a quick rush of air come past me and got the courage to open my eyes and look around to see what had happened. There, on the concrete floor in front of me, lay a trail of blood that led out the cafeteria door.

CHAPTER FOUR

I sat there staring silently at the bright red splatter of blood on the floor. A female staff member bent down and picked up my rusty metal cup while the male chaperone across the cafeteria shouted for all of us to line up again. I quickly did as ordered and fell into line formation. As we walked forward, I looked to my left and noticed the frail boy and a couple of others being left behind.

We walked down the cold, long hallway, but came to a halt midway.

I became excited as our line filed to the back door of the orphanage, because it meant I would get to go to school. The doors opened, and I followed the line leader, making my way outside. It was a freezing day, and I felt my body temperature decrease more and more as the cold wind blew through me.

The line paused, and I stood by the entrance of the orphanage, gazing out at the high, gray, concrete walls that surrounded my home. The only way out, as far as I knew, was through the big green gate straight ahead. On my right, toward the east, ran a long path. If I made my way down that trail, I could see on the right-hand side an open playground with a swing set that held three swings. If I kept straight on the path, it would come to a dead end, where an old Catholic church sat vacant. A black, wrought-iron fence surrounded the church. A big chain and lock sealed the gate.

From where I stood, the orphanage sat south of me. It had busted windows on the lower floor. The exterior walls had been painted a peach-like color, faded with years, contrasted the peeling forest-green trim on the windows and doors.

To the west of me lay the other wing of the L-shaped orphanage. On the west corner stood a concrete wall leaving just enough space for an alleyway. The only way in and out of this place was to have a staff member open the big green gate, which was way too difficult to open for someone as small as myself.

While I stood outside, observing my home, the stocky staff member came through the door behind us, giving us the cue to follow him to the big green gate. The gate squeaked on its hinges, the latches scraping on the bottom of the door as it slowly opened. Once we were given permission to exit, I stepped into another universe.

The cold wind blew without mercy, hitting me in the face and making me shiver. Some of my siblings walked briskly in front of me, but I strolled along. I did not hurry, but instead relished every step of temporary freedom.

I knew I needed to get to class, but I took my time anyway, looking through the windows of all the different stores I passed, mesmerized by the goodies they had to offer. The air was crisp with a hint of manure. Horses pulling wagons trotted up and down the cobblestones, and bicycles zoomed by, followed by the occasional car. Beer bottles littered the street. As various pedestrians scurried around me, I wondered if any of them had any idea what it was like to be me.

CHAPTER FIVE

I listened to the footsteps passing me on the cobblestone road as I strolled along, taking in the world outside the orphanage, a reality I hardly understood. I looked into a shop where chicken, ham, whole pigs, and cooked sausage hung on hooks in the front window. I wondered what it would be like to be able to cook and eat any one of the delicacies hanging there.

Next door was the bike shop. Here it was I really paused to dream. Surely one day I could own the two Pegas bikes on display in the bike shop window. They were somehow suspended so that they turned, glistening in the morning light. The bikes were black in color, dancing in circles as I watched them through the clear glass window. The light shimmered off their beautiful paint jobs, making me want them even more.

A gust of icy wind blew in my direction, and I turned my attention back toward my destination, and realized that all of my siblings were out of sight. I picked up speed; time was now of the essence. I could not be late for school.

As I gazed at the two-story building through the black, iron gates, I saw no one was in the front play yard. Only silence awaited me as I opened the gate to enter the school premises. The small, gray pebbles beneath my feet crunched with every step as I made my way up to the entrance and heaved open the big door. The foyer was dark as I entered, and silence greeted me within. I took a breath, only to get a whiff of the musty smell of children and chalk dust.

Slowly, I made my way up the stairs. With every stride, my footsteps echoed around the hallway. I paused for a moment and adjusted the left shoe on my right foot, only to hear the staircase below me squeak. Once I felt secure, I made my way upstairs, and soon arrived in front of my classroom door.

I was scared to face my classmates as I gazed nervously through the open door, debating whether I should enter. Maybe being absent might be better than being late again.

I could see Mrs. Andrea, my teacher, tampering with something on her desk. I watched her graceful movements. She was thin, with short, blond hair with some grays fading on each side. While I watched her, she sensed my presence, made eye contact with me, and waved me in.

I felt insecure as I made my way inside with every classmate's eye turned toward me. I felt exposed. I felt their contempt for me, the little orphan boy of no value, the one with ill-fitting clothes and shoes, while they were all dressed in their clean proper school attire.

I quickly looked down at the light wooden floor and selected a seat in the back, away from the stares, where I could feel invisible. As I made my way toward my seat, Mrs. Andrea said good morning to the class and turned around to write her name in cursive on the blackboard.

When she turned back, her facial features were stern, yet welcoming. Her blue eyes danced around the room. She spoke with intent and purpose as she lifted a chart with cursive letters on it. She instructed everyone to get paper and a pencil out of their desks, and all of my classmates lifted their desktops, as if in sync with some drummer I could not hear.

I followed their lead and lifted my desktop, expecting to find nothing within it, but as I looked inside, I smiled to myself. Dried bread crumbs were scattered everywhere. I reached in, wedging the crumbs into the corner. I hoped no one would notice as I scooped up the bread crumbs and placed them in my mouth.

CHAPTER SIX

While my classmates doodled on their papers as Mrs. Andrea spoke, I spaced out getting lost within my own imagination, riding down the cobblestone roads on my new black Pegas bike. The bell soon rang, bringing me back to reality, making my attention veer toward the front of the room where Mrs. Andrea sat at her desk, waving a bell back and forth to inform us it was time for recess.

As we made our way outside, I faded into the background, watching my classmates play tag. I felt as if I were a mayflower while I listened to the pebbles crunching beneath my classmates' feet, raising a little dust. My stomach started to growl, and a brilliant idea hit me. I asked Mrs. Andrea for permission to use the bathroom, and when she granted me the pass, I grinned to myself and headed inside.

I ran upstairs, sneaked back into the classroom, and searched all the desks for any food my fellow students might have left behind. I lifted every wooden desktop, hoping to find something to fill my tummy. I found my favorite, a salami sandwich, which seemed otherworldly in its deliciousness. I devoured it quickly, barely tasting the butter and meat. I then continued my hunt.

My next treasure was puzzling: a bread substance protected by a blue wrapper, the likes of which I had never seen before. I tore into the paper and took a big bite, only to be pleasantly surprised to find that it was filled with a rich, dark chocolate that tasted ever so sweet.

Hearing footsteps outside the classroom door, I closed the desk as quickly as I could and tried to hide my guilt as the classroom filled with children. Those terribly prying eyes were once more upon me. As Mrs. Andrea dismissed the others to their seats, she approached and asked me what I had done.

I said, "Nothing," and clenched the blue wrapper tightly in my hand as she reached for her ruler.

CHAPTER SEVEN

Mrs. Andrea demanded I hold out my left hand. I followed her instruction. However, in order to hide the evidence, I continued to clench my fist.

Whack! The first blow connected with the top of my left hand, startling me. I managed to block out the pain.

Whack! Whack!

I held the wrapper with all of my strength as the discipline continued, but soon my grip came loose, and the evidence dropped on the wooden floor. Tears rolled down my face while I miserably met the gaze of my classmates. Mrs. Andrea then grabbed me by my left ear, twisting it as she dragged me back to my desk. Heat and pain pulsed around the edge of my ear.

While I sat there, feeling alone, I gazed out the window, daydreaming once more in hope of escaping my reality. The bell soon rang again; class was over.

As I walked down the hall toward the stairs, every eye turned to me, filling me with paranoia and shame. I picked up my speed, heading down stairs, and once outside I sprinted for the gate, ignoring the stares of everyone around me.

I was once more free, safe from judgment, within the universe of the unknown. I felt more at ease, being alone. I walked along the side of the cobblestone streets, looking through the shop windows and dreaming of one day of owning all they displayed.

My stomach started rumbling, and I knew I needed to stop to eat something before heading home. I arrived at a dumpster and reached in, hoping to find a quick snack, maybe even my favorite: cabbage ends.

I dug through rotten potatoes and other unknown objects before finally finding some cabbage ends. I reveled in the discovery. I wiped any foreign substances from the cabbage ends and bit into the savory snack. I loved the crunch and all the flavors that surrendered to my palate as the cabbage filled my tummy.

After I finished my snack, I headed back to the orphanage, careful not to arouse suspicion in the staff, lest I receive further punishment. I arrived at the big green gate and knocked, hoping, in some part of my mind, that no one would answer. As I waited for the gate to open, I listened to the horses trotting by on the cobblestones and savored my last few moments of freedom. Soon, though, a staff member answered my summons.

I stepped through the gates of hell, back into my infernal universe. With my head bowed in silence, I silently begged the demons that resided within these walls to spare my life as I obeyed their commands.

As I walked through the gate, the cold wind blew on my face with a hint of sweet perfume. I looked up ever so gingerly, and suddenly joy filled me. There stood Olga, the owner, looking at me.

"Buna, Zoltan," she said.

I smiled and gazed into her beautiful hazel eyes, and her rose-red cheeks made dimples as she smiled back at me. Her teeth were beautifully white, and they stood out in contrast to her red lipstick and her long, beautiful dark-red hair. She held a bag in her hand. Smiling joyfully, she reached in it and handed me a small yellow egg container filled with goodies.

Behind her stood a couple of staff members, including the stocky man with the blue shirt and denim overalls a size too big. All the staff behind Olga seemed obedient and sly around her while she was with us. Nonetheless, I was awed by Olga's kindness. Regardless of the staff's presence, laying eyes on her, or even saying her name, gave me solace.

Olga looked back up at the staff and called Costin by name.

She waved over the stocky, brown little man and told him to get us inside, out of the cold weather. Olga said goodbye to all of us and headed her way. Trepidation came over us as we headed back to the orphanage with Costin and the rest of the staff. I could feel the heat coming out of the steam column radiator as we passed by it, making our way down the long hallway and back upstairs.

I felt scared and out of control as we arrived at two large white doors that squeaked as they opened. Once they were fully ajar, we were led inside a big white room that was set up like a chapel with six rows of dark wooden benches on each side. The pews bore teeth and claw marks, and the atmosphere stank with the lingering odors of urine and fear.

To the left of me stood a fireplace with a metal baseplate. The grate-like panel, which I had never seen used, was made with an open, interwoven design. The wall on my right held one small window, which gave just enough light for me to see. The rest of the space, however, was surrounded by plain white walls, punctured by scattered holes.

As I entered, Costin asked me to hand him the treat Olga had given me. Reluctantly, I did as he asked, in order to avoid punishment. Once I gave him what he wanted, I was directed to sit on a particular bench. I sat and started rocking back and forth. The big white doors squeaked behind me once more and closed with a bang, giving me goose bumps as the fear in the room grew with ferocity.

CHAPTER EIGHT

The energy of terror in the room escalated. No one had to say anything; everyone felt it. I looked down at the scratched wooden floor as I kept rocking in an attempt to comfort and calm myself. I knew inherently that evil lingered within this place, and was almost tangible in the atmosphere.

There was silence throughout the room. The only thing I could hear was the air passing back and forth as I rocked in place. Footsteps sounded louder as a staff member made his way closer to me.

A single cry erupted in the room. It grew louder by the second, and with it my fear. My heartbeat increased as I doggedly looked around, searching for the source of the cry. Costin and another male staff member had dragged a young girl into the middle of the room. She was thin, with pale, white skin. Her hair was a little longer than shoulder-length, slightly curly, and brown.

She tried to fight them off as they kicked her and beat her with sticks. She cried out with the little bit of energy that hadn't been starved out of her. I watched, terrified, as her cries grew fainter, while the sticks whooshing through the air, making contact with her body, became louder with every lash. The quieter she got, the more slowly I rocked myself back and forth, until she was silent, and I was still.

A kind of shock settled over me, and I picked up the speed of my rocking again to the point that I became lightheaded from the effort and almost passed out. My world spun around me, but I did what I knew best: I stayed silent. I felt a part of me die with her as I sat there, knowing there was nothing I could do as she struggled, gasping for air.

A terrible thought came to me as minutes squeezed by, feeling like hours. I envied the girl. I wished it were me, lying on that floor. I feared dying, yet with the way my life was going, I was also afraid of living.

CHAPTER NINE

Costin and the other male staff member snatched the girl off the floor by her upper arm, then sat her on the floor next to the nearest bench as she moaned in pain. After a minute or two passed—it seemed like hours—they yelled that it was time for dinner, and instructed all of us to get in line.

I did as ordered, and we all made our way back downstairs toward the cafeteria as one. As we entered the cafeteria, the staff commanded us to form a line in front of the kitchen window. As we shuffled ever so slowly to get our food, I looked around in surprise because there were tables and chairs with metal spoons at every place setting. This was different than usual.

I could smell the sweet fragrance of Olga lingering in the space. I wondered if this were her doing, but as I looked around I could not see her. I finally made my way to the kitchen window and peeped through it, in hope of finding her. Three large women stood back there; Olga was nowhere to be found. I watched the other ladies intently as I waited for my food. Two of them were doing other tasks, while the other one handed me a rusty metal bowl with some bread and water mixed together, mimicking some form of stew.

I smiled as I received my food and sat down as commanded, eating my dinner in utter silence. I could hear the metal spoons scraping against my siblings' teeth as they cleaned their plates. We sat there as one, hoping for our survival. With every bite we each knew our lives could be undone at any time, within the next few seconds, hours, or days.

The silence was interrupted by the sounds of one of my younger brothers as he got up to run around carelessly, shortly making his way to me. He placed his hand on the edge of my plate and scooped up the remainder of my dinner. He had a forest-green shirt on, with jean shorts that were full of diarrhea, which ran down both of his legs. I could smell the foul stink as he stared into my eyes with no comprehension of what was to come next, while he bounced in place rapidly with snot running down his nose. He made moaning noises, licking his fingers as some of my food fell through his deformed hand, then continued grinding his teeth and bouncing in place with no worry.

I watched him in amazement as a chaperone made his way toward us, snatching the nearest metal spoon on his way. Once he arrived at my table, he grabbed my brother's deformed hand and started beating it. The scant remains of the food in his hand fell on the floor. I could hear the metal of the spoon colliding with his knuckles as he cried and screamed with every whack. Tears streamed down his face, as I stared helplessly into his little brown eyes, listening to the spoon come in contact with his hand. I could see he did not understand his punishment.

After the male staff member was satisfied, he ceased his grip and yelled it was time for showers. I acted quickly, pushing my plate away from me and getting into line, to head back upstairs.

There, we were led to the bathroom area, where one tub sat.

After we were all corralled inside, we started taking off our clothes as we had been told, piling them in the middle of the yellow and white patterned tile floor. The stench of urine and feces filled the room from the soiled clothes. The silence seemed so much louder as the ragged, sheer breaths of my family echoed off the walls.

After I undressed, I wrapped my arms around myself, feeling the cold, while preparing for the worst as the female staff walked around, checking each of us to make sure we were fully stripped before picking up our clothes.

As I stood there, staring at the bathtub with one light hanging over it, I could hear footsteps behind me echo louder and louder. Costin and a tall, lanky man passed us, carrying a silver milk can. They headed toward the bathtub with intent and dumped the milk can full of hot water into our tub.

I watched them in amazement as they poured out the hot water, which produced a cloud of steam that hovered over us, mixing with the chills on our skin. Once the two men had stepped aside, two of my siblings in the front of the line went in as commanded by the female staff. The first one screamed as she placed her right foot in it. She hesitated, looking at the female staff member to her left. Without mercy, the woman grabbed the small-framed girl and placed her in the tub as she screamed in agony from being scorched by the hot water.

After both girls entered, they were given one scrub to wash one another from head to toe in full view of the female staff member who sat in a metal chair by the tub. When they were finished, a new couple would enter, and the line crept along in this fashion. My palms grew clammy and my heart raced with each step I took toward the used water.

Then it was my turn. I arrived at the edge of the tub, trying to keep it together as I first placed my left foot, then my right foot into the tub. Slowly I submerged myself into the slimy, dirty water. The water had only a slight hint of warmth remaining. It was thick and foul with the urine, grime, and feces of those who had been in the water before me.

Jula, one of my brothers, joined me. He was probably five feet, two inches in height, slightly thin in frame. He had brown eyes and blond hair, with a hint of freckles on his face and body. The water rose slightly as he entered, creating movement which in turn stirred some of the feces at the bottom of the water.

Fear of making a mistake agitated me as I grabbed the small white-handled scrub brush and applied it to his body. I went in a circular motion, scrubbing his legs, knees, and abdomen. Once I got everything I could with him sitting down, he stood. I dipped the small white scrub brush back into the soiled water before gently applying it to his back. I took a deep breath through my nostrils, trying to hide my uneasiness. I put the scrubber down and he turned back around to face me. I cupped my hands, filled them with water, and gently applied it to his genitals, as the small bits of feces floated around me.

Suddenly, pain sprung from the back of my head as the female staff member yanked me out of the tub by the crown of my hair. She started kicking me with her pointy, black Raoul Pop shoes. I squealed with every lash as the echo of my cries ricocheted off the yellow tiles, creating more noise.

I struggled, trying to block the assault to the best of my ability, but my body soon grew pliant and at ease from weakness as I tried to figure out what I had done wrong.

CHAPTER TEN

I lay on the cold, yellow bathroom floor tile, a chill coursing through my body while the pain in the pit of my stomach intensified. I shifted slightly, trying to ignore the blows as the chaperone kept kicking me. The pain seemed to burn regardless of what I did; there was no escape. My head pounded in rhythm to the beating of my heart, confirming that I was still alive, but with every pulse the pain seemed to intensify.

Once the beating ceased, I tried to wiggle against the pain that had formed in my stomach. My genitals screamed with agony, but there was to be no reprieve.

The woman snatched me up by my hair.

"Go to the center of the room," she said.

I stood up, trying to block out the pain. I did as she commanded. I held my jaws clenched tight, to keep the sound of agony from escaping, and slowly made my way to the staff member in the next room, where the pile of pajamas lay.

After I selected a pair of underwear and a T-shirt, I sat on the wooden floor, trying to get myself together. I pulled my underwear on while trying to ensure that the pain didn't increase in my lower stomach or my genitals.

The young female staff member who brought our clothes in the morning led me to the furthest back room. She then sat me down at one of the beds and told me that was where I would sleep.

I hated being in the darkest part of the bedrooms, but I nodded and slowly pulled my torn, foul blanket up as I lay down. I shifted slightly, trying to ease the pain in my stomach. When I pulled the blanket over me, it released an aroma of urine. The mattress brought me some comfort, but I knew that in order to decrease the pain, I must try to be still.

I lay there without moving, and once the room was filled with my other siblings, the staff turned the lights off. Minutes passed and I could not sleep, so I tried to rock my head back and forth on my pillow, as I had many times before. The motion just aggravated the pain in my stomach and increased my headache.

I attempted to fight through it, but I hadn't the resolve, and instead ended up rolling into a fetal position. With no other way to calm my nerves and soothe my pain, I began to suck my thumb, rubbing my index finger across the space between my top lip and nose like a baby. In my mind, and perhaps with what little strength was left for a quiet voice, I repeated her name, "Olga . . . Olga . . . Olga," until I slowly drifted into the fitful sleep of a wounded body and soul.

CHAPTER ELEVEN

I awoke a short time later, in the middle of the night, surrounded by pitch blackness. My stomach ached and my bladder was full. I knew I needed to use the plastic bin that lay in the middle of the floor, but I was scared of the darkness.

I rubbed my eyes to see a little more clearly, trying to spot the potty. I got distracted, though, because a woman not of this world, slightly heavyset and wearing a black cloth dress, stood in the darkness of the room with a white aura surrounding her.

I looked at her in awe, and she must have felt my presence, for her gaze veered in my direction. My heart raced, and my fear skyrocketed. I grabbed my blanket and pulled it over my head, trying to hide from that which I didn't understand.

I waited under my blanket for a few minutes, then cautiously peeked out. I wanted to prove that what I saw was only an illusion. Yet there she was, hovering up and down the aisle at the foot of my brothers' and sisters' beds. I hid under my blanket once more, knowing better than to peek again.

I tried to ignore my body's pain and go back to sleep. I could only manage the pain for a few more minutes. I knew I was not going to take a chance to get out of my bed. With my blanket still over my head,

I decided to secrete my waste in the hope that would put my stomach at ease. I lay in my foul stink, afraid to peek out again, and slowly but surely managed to fall back asleep.

I soon awoke to an alarm clock of shouts as the staff made their way through each bedroom. The howls of morning cries increased around me, growing louder the closer the staff came to my bedroom. I sprang up in my bed. Hoping to lessen my punishment, I crossed my feet. Regardless of what I did to try to prevent retribution, I knew I was guilty. I sat motionless on my bed, awaiting for what was to come as the stink of urine and feces fermented around me.

Soon two female chaperones made their way toward me, and I knew they could smell my foul stench as they approached. They pulled me out of bed by my hair, and my scalp exploded with pain. I screamed as they jerked me onto the dark wood floor, then dragged me the length of the bedroom.

The smell of my feces intensified, filling my lungs as it smeared down the backs of my thighs. The women dragged me into a small bathroom I had never seen before. They released their grip on my hair and started beating me and kicking me. The only thing I could do was scream in agony, hoping it would all end soon.

My scream echoed off the green and white tile floor, but I soon became limp from weakness, and the beating ceased. I lay there without energy while pain coursed through every inch of my body. I felt my body jerk as my underwear was pulled off forcibly. I cried, trying to catch my breath, but without any form of reprieve, my dirty garment, full of feces and urine, filled my face. One of them pressed it there forcibly and held it in place.

I tried to hold my breath, and tried to escape—I was wild with pain and weakness—but regardless of what I did, the feces entered my nostrils and mouth. I could taste the foulness of my waste as the garment was being emptied. I lay on the green and white bathroom floor, still and hopeless, as the staff turned on a black hose.

The water was cold. I rolled over on my left side in a fetal position as the mess was blasted off me. I watched the feces stream past my head, toward the floor drain. I lay there forlorn, wishing they had finished me off. The pain and discomfort coursed through my body with every beat of the brutal spray. Instead, they grabbed me once more and dragged me back to the rest of the orphans, where the clean pile of clothes lay.

CHAPTER TWELVE

I lay there naked and petrified as my siblings walked around me to get their clothes. I could still smell the feces as I contemplated whether I should even try to get up and dress myself. I knew that if I didn't do as asked, further punishment could follow. I lifted myself ever so cautiously. A sharp pain shot through my stomach and groin. I stood still for a second or two, then gradually tried to make my way to the pile of clothes.

Once I picked out my attire, from what little selection remained, I stayed right there and dressed myself with the scant coordination I had left, rather than waste my energy on going back to my bed. While I struggled to put on a long-sleeved shirt that was much too big for me, Costin and another male staff member—this one thin, with curly, thick, black hair and a light-brown complexion—came through the other bedroom doors, yelling for all of us to get in line. I panicked, rushing to slip on my shirt while an aching pain shot through my back and stomach. I tried to cope with it regardless, and finally managed to get myself dressed.

I got up to get in line, but as I made my way to my siblings my groin pain escalated with each step I took. I gritted my teeth while I walked down the stairs and followed the line to the cafeteria. We soon arrived at our destination, and I looked around. The room was filled with new, round tables surrounded by chairs. We were corralled inside, and a female staff member commanded me to sit at the table by the fireplace, in the back, near the entrance door. I was so thankful I didn't have to walk further. I did just as she asked. I sat in silence, finding a reprieve from my pain. I looked around, awed by the new table and chairs.

A large white female staff member from the kitchen started making her way toward me with some bread and water. I gingerly held my hand out. With thanks, I glanced up at her. Her unique white headscarf almost made me smile. After she turned around, I started devouring my food, but as I gasped for air with every bite I could smell a hint of feces—the aftermath of my morning experience. Nonetheless, I demolished my breakfast, bowed my head after I was finished, and waited for my cup to get picked up.

With my head down I stared at the crumbs of bread that had fallen on the table. Soon I heard footsteps, louder and louder, growing closer to my table. I knew I needed to wait for the rush of air that signaled the staff member had gotten my cup or gone past me, but I felt nothing. I decided to take a chance and looked up to take a peek. A female staff member was standing next to me and grabbed my left arm, lifting me up. She led me out the cafeteria doors, down the long hallway. With every step my genital pain increased as my heart bounded rapidly as she dragged me along at her side, walking too fast for me to keep up.

My genitals ached, and my mind went crazy with worry, for with every stride we took, I feared that my worst nightmare had come true, and that I would never return . . . or that I would.

CHAPTER THIRTEEN

I was terrified of what was to come. My body had started to get accustomed to the pain as the chaperone walked briskly, dragging me along. She banked left, arriving at an office door before releasing her grip. She paused long enough to make an attempt to tame her brown hair, getting herself together with a façade before knocking on the frosted glass window of the door.

Within seconds after the first knock, Olga answered the door with a smile. Her sweet perfume greeted me, filling my nostrils and intermixing with my odor. Still, her scent made my anxiousness come to a halt. She stood at the doorway and smiled at me gently. Then she dismissed the staff member, and her eyes met mine.

She motioned for me to sit on the black leather couch that faced her desk, and as I entered the room, her scent engulfed me. I hopped up on the comfortable black couch, trying to not give away that my body ached. Once I was comfortable, I started rubbing the couch with my hand, mesmerized by the way it felt. I drank in the white, glamorously bright walls before turning my attention to Olga.

Tranquility settled over the room as Olga made her way to her desk. It was made of brown wood, and she had some paperwork nicely organized in front of her. As she sat down, she broke the silence.

"Zoltan, do you know why you're here in my office?" she asked.

I shook my head "no" as she smiled at me with her beautiful white teeth. Ever so gracefully, she came around her desk, sat next to me, and looked at me with excitement in her sincere, beautiful eyes.

"You're going to be adopted," she whispered.

I sat stunned in silence, trying to process this information. I tuned into the only word that had struck me: *adopted.* It was going to happen. It was going to happen to me.

I had heard this word from my siblings and staff. I felt joyous, happy, and shocked as I waited, gleefully, for my new parents to come through the doors of her office and take me home, right then and there. I gazed at the door with anticipation, hoping that my new family would come right then as Olga gave me a hug, while rubbing me on the back of my head.

I flinched from the pain I still felt, and with hesitation she asked about the knot she could feel there and how I got it. I wanted to tell her, to confide in her, but I was still afraid for my life. I stuttered, trying to come up with something as I looked down toward the carpet.

"I fell. Outside. And hit my head."

She stared at me suspiciously for a few seconds before giving me another hug. Then she reassured me once more that my parents would be coming soon to take me to America.

I didn't understand why they didn't just come through the door right then. Nonetheless, I was overwhelmed with excitement and relief. I knew I was soon to be rescued.

After Olga broke the great news, she told me not to tell anyone, and then took me back to the cafeteria as my brothers and sisters were getting in line. When we walked in, every gaze settled on Olga's smiling face. As I stood next to her, I could see the fear in the eyes of the other children, and the desire to be rescued lived in their spark. Olga waved at them with true grace, saying "hello" and bringing them joy.

She dismissed me to join the others. I bowed my head as Olga turned back around, heading her own way, and I fell in line with the others. I was excited by the news of my adoption, but I didn't want to show it; I was afraid of being punished. I just had to last one more weekend, and then I would be with my real family. Or maybe it would even happen tomorrow.

I'm going to be adopted, I kept repeating to myself as we walked upstairs. However, once we made it up the stairs we were shifted to go toward the big white room, and a shiver of fear ran down my spine. I realized it was going to be a long day.

CHAPTER FOURTEEN

I tried desperately to be more obedient than ever as I focused on surviving the next couple of days, until my new family came to my rescue. I sat on the bench, just as I was commanded to do. As I rocked back and forth, trying to keep a positive, calm mindset, I imagined my new life, one with no fear of pain. But as I did, the two big white doors closed behind me with a bang.

Instantly the pit of my stomach filled with a feeling of hopelessness. However, I would keep repeating Olga's promise to myself as a staff member with chiseled features lit a cigarette and went up and down the aisle, examining us. The reflection of the bright orange tip of the cigarette glowed in his small beady eyes every time he took a drag, and trepidation filled the room. The smell of cigarette smoke filled the atmosphere, overpowering the smell of feces as a hush settled over us.

A whimper soon chimed in, filling the room as the male chaperone with the cigarette dragged a little boy from the front benches. I looked and saw that it was the boy who had been scooping my food with his hands in the cafeteria. My brother's moans and screams echoed as the male staff member dragged him to the back of the room, toward the fireplace. I stopped my rocking and sat still, trying to see what would happen.

I watched the male staff member take a seat in a chair, still holding on to the boy. My brother gritted his teeth back and forth, bouncing in place and yelling. The staff member took another drag of his cigarette, then grabbed my small-framed brother, sat him on his lap, and blew the smoke in his face as he chuckled.

My brother tried to squirm out of his grip, but the man simply took his right arm while creating another red cherry tip, and placed the tip of the cigarette on his forearm. The little boy screamed, tears rolling down his face, while the staff member gave a smoky laugh.

I started rocking back and forth again, telling myself everything was going to be okay; I was going to America. As I held my arms against my chest, the thought *it could have been me* came across my consciousness.

The staff member kept messing with the boy, placing his fingers in his mouth and biting down on them, making my brother scream out loud once more. The speed of my rocking back and forth accelerated as I tried to hold in my emotions and struggled to keep silent. Suddenly the big white doors creaked open, making everything come to a pause as the light flooded in from outside.

CHAPTER FIFTEEN

I put a hold on my rapid movement and turned around, hoping it was my new family coming to my rescue. It was a female staff member, come to let us know it was time for our naps. The chaperone stood up, screaming for us to get in line. Once everyone did as we were instructed, we exited the room, banking right toward the bedrooms. I shuffled along in the line as we were guided to different beds.

This round, I got the privilege of sleeping in the middle of the bedroom, away from the darkness, where the natural light flooded in from outside through the windows. As I hopped in my bed, lying down with my clothes still on, I waited for the staff's footsteps to cease before I could feel at ease.

When silence settled over all the rooms I started daydreaming of America. I remember rocking my head back and forth on the pillow, repeating Olga's name under my breath. Mentally, I was creating the perfect image of my new life. My body relaxed as I slowly drifted in and out of that light daytime sleep. Soon footsteps from the distance interrupted, especially as they grew louder and louder.

I tensed up and was fully awake as the sound made its way closer to my room. I tried to see where the noise was coming from. The steps stopped abruptly, as little moans of my brother or sister sounded near me. I wondered what was taking place. I decided to slowly and quietly roll over onto my stomach. My heart beat rapidly as I looked left and then right.

My brother Gage on my left was just staring at the ceiling, while my other brother on my right had fallen asleep. I contemplated whether I should seek the source of the cry. I finally rallied the strength to peek over the scratched wooden headboard to see where the whimpering was coming from. A few feet away, near the fireplace, was a boy writhing in his bed as the two staff members stood over him.

When I looked into my brother's blue eyes I knew that he was afraid. I tried to breathe discreetly, but could hear my own breath getting heavier while the two staff members ripped off his blanket. The boy lay there terrified, not sure what to do as he squirmed in his bed. Without mercy, they started hitting him all over his body, making the whimpering echo into loud cries.

Olga, please come save us, was the only thought going through my head as the two young male staff members took the boy by his arms and feet.

My brother's cries turned into screams. Meanwhile, the two men started to swing him side to side like it was some sort of game. His body was their toy, and he had no defense against them.

CHAPTER SIXTEEN

Olga, please come rescue us. Please come rescue us.

I heard both of the staff members counting as they swung him side to side.

"One!"

Please, Olga, please come rescue us.

Time seemed to move slowly as I lay there hearing, "Two!"

I waited for a miracle and took a deep breath, trying not to give myself away, hoping to smell Olga's sweet fragrance so that she may come to the rescue.

"Three!"

The room filled with an eerie silence, and I put my head down in panic. I heard my brother trying to gasp for air. My mind went haywire. Finally, I got myself together enough to peek over my scratched wooden bed once more. There, on the scarred wooden floor near the fireplace, was blood coming from my brother's forehead. I put my head down in panic as tears fell from my eyes and emotions engulfed me. I tried to take shallow breaths, to keep silent, in the hope I wouldn't give myself away.

I soon became exhausted from silently weeping and turned on my side, placing my thumb in my mouth to soothe myself. It almost worked. As I dozed in and out, I could nearly shut down the panic inside. A shout from a staff member soon woke me, and I realized there would be no dreaming through this reality, for fear was a writhing, constant presence. I shot up and got out of bed, getting myself together before getting in line, even as my heart bounded and my mind went in all directions.

I finally made my way to the line, and as I stood there, trying to calm myself, I looked around discreetly in hope of finding my injured brother. I looked behind me and in front of me, but there was no sign of him. Maybe he was further up the line, I thought to myself, as the line started to shuffle forward and a staff member corralled us toward the cafeteria.

CHAPTER SEVENTEEN

Once we arrived at our destination, I sat eating my "stew" as my mind buzzed with confusion, worry, and above all, fear. I prayed for something different, for Olga to burst through the door with my new family before the night ended. I listened to the scraping of the spoons around me. But as time ticked by, my wish fizzled into reality. The staff shouted for us to get back in line.

As we headed back upstairs, I hated my circumstances more and more, knowing that a better life was yet to come. To my surprise, we were led to a section of the bathroom I had never used before. The surroundings mimicked the other bathrooms—it had the same yellow tile as the bathroom with the tub, next door to the left—however, in this room, on the left and right side were three shower stalls.

Costin made us take our clothes off while he went into each shower stall and turned on the water. Then we threw our dirty garments in the center of the room. We stood there, nude and silent, wondering what this new system was, as Costin made his way around instead of a female staff member.

Once he finished turning on the water, he took off his own clothes and then steered three to four of us into each stall to take a shower. I stood in the back of the line, looking at my brothers and sisters as their bodies shivered. I was waiting for my turn when suddenly a little way in front of me, a sister of mine, black in color, caught my attention.

I gazed at her dark, creamy complexion. Her eyes were dark brown, and her hair was short, black, and curly. I gazed at her chest with curiosity, for I had never seen breasts like hers before. I moved toward her, breaking out of the line as I became curious. I stared at her female anatomy with wonder, while some of my brothers eyed me, before joining me, as we headed her way. She lifted her arms toward her chest to cover her breasts, but regardless of what she tried to do, we pressed toward her.

I lunged forward, grabbing her right breast with my hand. I squeezed it with all the strength I had, only to discover that which I didn't understand. My brothers soon joined in and we dragged her onto the floor, groping her as she whimpered before crying out louder, the sound soon overpowering the other noises around us.

Her cries reached the depth of my existence, making me feel her pain more the louder she got. I quickly relinquished my hold on her, and remorse settled in the pit of my stomach. While I got back in line, I battled back and forth within my mind about the action I had just committed, wondering whether what I had done was wrong. As I looked, I saw that she still lay on the floor. It was apparent to me that I had caused her great pain.

I looked down on the yellow tile floor, ashamed of myself, as Costin came out of one of the showers, making his presence known as he walked toward me. I stood there quietly as he made his way. I was ready for any punishment I had to endure.

Once he was within arm's reach he grabbed me and three others and led us into an empty shower stall. I stood in the shower awkwardly, with three of my brothers, waiting for my punishment as the warm water fell on us. To my surprise, Costin merely stood there and watched us. I slowly moved around in hopes of getting the rest of my body underneath the water, but my body collided with the other boys' bodies every time I fought for the water to fall on me. Tired of trying to maneuver my way around, I stood still and let the water fall where it would on me as it transitioned from mildly warm to cold.

Without hesitation, Costin yanked me out of the shower, almost making me fall. I stood there, awaiting my punishment, as he looked me up and down. Yet he only dismissed me to the center of the bedroom, where a pile of underwear and pajamas lay on a big white sheet. I was surprised that I was in the clear. I dressed quickly to get warm, then awaited my next command.

A few minutes after I'd gotten myself dressed, a female chaperone approached, grabbed me by my left arm, and dragged me to one of the bedrooms. We passed the center area where the light was always lit, and soon arrived at the second room, where an extra bed lay empty.

She sat me on the edge of the bed and informed me this was where I would sleep. I nodded and lay down, pulling the torn, stained blanket up to my neck. I was grateful to be sleeping one door down from the center of the room, where the night light shimmered in the darkness.

The female staff member turned around to leave the room. I could hear her footsteps on the wooden floor as she headed for the light switch and turned the overhead light off. As I lay there with yet another urine-stained blanket pulled up to my neck, I blinked rapidly in order to attune to the darkness. Within seconds, I could see. Once the nervousness from being in the dark settled, I began to sway my head back and forth, trying to focus on happy thoughts of a new family. However, my mind still raced with doubt, for pain and fear were much more prominent than happiness in my experience.

I hoped for a good ending, but I wondered why it took so long to be free.

I feared death, but more than that, I feared an unexpected demise. I would have preferred to meet it head-on, rather than have it sneak up on me during the night, finding me while I slept, unaware.

CHAPTER EIGHTEEN

I put my thumb in my mouth while rubbing the tip of my nose with my index finger, soothing myself as I slowly rocked my head back and forth. I couldn't stop my mind from racing, regardless of what I did; therefore, I gradually started to pick up speed with my rocking until I was dizzy. Then I was able to drift off to sleep.

I awoke in the middle of the night, my stomach unsettled because of intensifying pain. The sound of clattering echoed from the middle of the room, making me feel uneasy. Afraid, I lay there still and quiet. I blinked, hoping my eyes would adjust to the light coming from the next room, so that I could see my enemy as he or she approached.

I then heard the noise of the can shifting once more from the center of the room. I focused my attention in that direction. My eyes soon adjusted, and I could see one of my brothers in the distance, using the potty tray in the middle of the room. Once he finished, I saw him come my way, as if he knew I was looking at him. He soon arrived at the right side of my bed. I lay there quietly, trying not to give myself away, trying to figure out what he was doing. He then turned around, naked, and sat on the edge of my bed. I could feel my covers and mattress move rapidly as he shimmied back and forth, and it hit me that he was wiping the remains of his feces on the edge of my bed.

Once he finished, I contemplated whether I should try to empty my bowels, too, to at least ease my stomach. After a few minutes of contemplation, I decided to get up and tiptoe my way toward the bin in the middle of the room. The closer I got to the pan, the wetter my feet became as urine and feces squished beneath my feet. Still determined to empty my bowels, I sat on the potty. Feces and urine ran past my feet as it overflowed, going between my toes. After I finished using the can, I looked around for a way to clean myself, but with no other option, I did as I had learned. I made my way toward someone's bed and shimmied the remains of my feces on the edge of the sheets before heading back to my own bed.

My bowels were finally at ease, and I hopped back into my bed, snuggling into the covers as I wiped my feet on my sheets. I was giddy as I placed my thumb in my mouth. It did not wreak of the smell or have the horrible taste of my own defecation, which would have been on my hand if I hadn't wiped it on the mattress. Soon, I had rocked myself back and forth into a good night's sleep.

Morning came, and the room was filled with quiet laughter. I wondered what was taking place, and I rubbed my eyes to see what the commotion was about. The smell of feces and urine was present as always. However, morning sun peeked through the windows across from me. When my eyes adjusted, I gazed out at the uproar and saw my siblings hopping up and down on their beds. Dust particles hung in the air, made more prominent by the sun's rays, and the children bounced on their beds, chuckling and swatting at the mysterious particles dancing around them.

CHAPTER NINETEEN

Everyone knew that today was the day we would get to play outside. We tried to keep our voices down, in spite of our excitement. Soon the screaming of staff voices echoed from the bedroom next door, along with the clacking of their sticks hitting the edges of beds. I reached down towards my pants, to ensure that I didn't foul myself, and to my surprise I was dry. I knew this round I was going to be safe, as the chaperones made their way into the room.

One went to the center of the room and dropped the big sheet, while the other staff member looked around to make sure everyone was awake. As she made her way around, I propped myself up to ensure no harm would be done. The female chaperone in the center of the room undid the sheet, giving us permission to head toward the pile of clothes. As I hopped out of bed and made my way to the center, I realized the fresh clothes lay in the feces and urine that had spilled over from the bin the night before.

Nonetheless, I grabbed some denim overalls, shoes, and a shirt a size too big from the top of the pile, and made my way back to the edge of the bed to dress myself. Last, I put on a pair of white shoes. The sole of the right shoe was torn, but I was grateful, as I tied my laces, that at least I got a pair that matched this time. Once we all finished dressing ourselves, the chaperones yelled for us to get in line, and we were all corralled toward the stairs.

In the cafeteria, I did as I was told, and sat to await my food. When the bread and water arrived, I devoured them as fast as possible. I couldn't wait for the day to start. The excitement of playing on the swing set couldn't come soon enough, especially since the other option was to stay inside. I looked around, listening to my siblings drinking their water and chewing their bread, wishing they would hurry. Time stood still, as if it knew of my anticipation.

I sat impatiently, waiting for the staff member to yell for us to get in line. Finally, she did. Her voice was music to my ears, and I stood without hesitation, doing as I was asked. After all of us formed a line, we were directed down the long hallway before banking right, to the green glass door. As I stood there, filled with sheer anticipation, I could feel a slight breeze coming through the bottom-right corner of the door's broken glass. Feeling the air coming in from outside made me ever more excited. The door couldn't open soon enough. We sprinted forward like a herd of cattle down a chute, while the sun's rays met us outside.

We all went different ways. I sprinted east down the concrete path, past the two big tires filled with different-colored pansies, rushing toward the swing set. I could hear the flapping of my shoes below me with every stride I took, but I didn't want to slow down. I was determined to get a swing. I was the first to make it to my destination, and I took a seat to reserve my spot in the center swing. My brothers and sisters followed.

Once I sat comfortably, I sighed with relief. I grabbed both chains and stepped back, to give myself some momentum. I released my hold, allowing gravity to take over. Joy came over me. I swayed my legs back and forth, back and forth, to reach the highest elevation, as butterflies swirled in the depths of my stomach. I chuckled, as if I were being tickled, while the laws of physics took over, pushing me back and forth on the swing as I gazed up into the firmament.

As I looked up at the wonderful blue sky, with patches of white and gray clouds, my inner self was awed as I acknowledged there was something greater than me. I was fascinated with that which couldn't be explained. All around, my brothers and sisters were laughing in the background as they played in nature. The noise of their laughter was soon eclipsed by the blowing of a whistle to the left of me, on the other side of the concrete wall surrounding the orphanage.

I ceased my swinging, tuning into the sound, which I had never heard before. Some of my siblings went to the wall, curious. I lingered, afraid to give up my swing, and watched my brothers and sisters help each other climb up the wall. Some ran up, grabbing ahold of the ledge and pulling themselves up to see what was happening on the other side. The swings next to me soon became empty, and my curiosity brewed as the whistle blew once more. I didn't want to give up my spot, but the spirit of inquiry nudged me, eventually making me give in and go to the wall.

I stared at the tall concrete edifice, wondering how I could manage to make my way up there like the others who stood on it. I remembered what I'd seen others do, and since I didn't have anyone at the bottom to give me a push, as I saw some do, I would have to try to mimic the pulling-up method. I took a few steps back, to get some distance between myself and the wall, then I ran to it at full speed and jumped with my left foot out. But I could barely touch the top of the ledge. I stepped back once more, rubbing the left knee I'd scraped, and stared at the wall, visualizing my next course of action. After a few minutes, I ran toward the wall once more, placing my left foot on the wall, and then my right, to propel myself a little higher.

As I did, I heard a tearing sound. But I had made it; I hung on the ledge of the wall with both hands. I pulled myself up with all my strength, and once I'd made it to the top successfully, I looked down and saw that the sole of my right shoe had completely ripped off.

CHAPTER TWENTY

I hung on the ledge, with my chest pressed against the concrete wall, and stared down in amazement at the men standing in a line formation with their backs toward us. They all wore matching gray shirts and dark green pants. The one facing them—evidently the leader—wore a green jacket with a drab, olive-colored wool hat. He glanced in our direction, and, seeing us there, blew the whistle I'd heard from a distance.

The men facing him started to do jumping jacks in rhythm as one. I gazed at them in awe. I looked to my right. A short distance away stood two men wearing the same uniform as the one leading the group. They were guarding a black iron gate that seemed to roll on wheels. The men had perfect straight-back posture as they each held a PA md. 86 assault rifle with a sharp-looking bayonet affixed to the barrel. The sight of the guns sent chills down my spine. The commander blew the whistle once more, and the men ceased their jumping jacks.

What was this place? The commander shouted an order to his men, though I could not understand what he was saying from a distance. He blew the whistle again, and the men broke out of their formal line. They started heading toward the perimeter of the wall, running laps around their facility. My siblings and I gazed in amazement as they made their way around, heading toward us, waving and smiling every time they passed. I chuckled with the others, cheering them on while they entertained us with every lap they made.

The whistle sounded again, but much longer this time, as the men formed back in line to face their commander once more. Once they'd all fallen back into formation, the one in command saluted the soldiers, and then turned around, evidently heading to his office or his quarters. Once the sergeant was no longer in sight, the men started to break off in different directions, without any form of order, and headed into their bunker. While my siblings began to make their way off the wall, I decided to stay with a couple of others. I gazed at the men guarding the gate, waiting for them to break out of order. However, they stayed in place. I did the same. Hoping to see another form of adventure, I lingered, in awe of what I'd just seen.

From a distance, across the empty base, a white man with short brown hair came out of the quarters and headed our way. He was six-foot-three at least, and 200 pounds of muscle as he strode toward us. I'd hoped for another show, but not like this. My heart started to beat rapidly, intimidated and afraid of what the man might do. As he made his way closer, a smile appeared, and my anxiety soon subsided. He held something in his left hand, hidden in a white napkin. The sight of it made my curiosity grow. His smile radiated. Once he was in arm's reach, he revealed the mystery beneath the napkin—a pastry of some sort. He broke off pieces and began passing them out to the ones who had stayed.

He stooped over a little, to be at eye level with me, smiling. I smiled back with anticipation as he gave me a piece of his treat before moving down the line. I gazed at the sweet goodie in wonder, not knowing what exactly it was. The treat was filled with caramelized apples, and covered with a white cream sauce. I had never seen anything like it. I devoured it, relishing every morsel. The taste was sweet and savory, and it lingered on my palate, making me want even more. I gazed at the man, hoping for more, but it was all gone. The man smiled at us, wiping his hands before waving at us and heading back into his quarters.

After a few seconds of silence, I hopped off the concrete wall, still elated by the entertainment and the treat. When I gazed around, the swing sets were empty. I looked to see what my brothers and sisters were doing, and saw they were heading south, where the orphanage stood. I wondered why, for dinner was not even close. Then I heard a female staff member yelling in the distance, calling all of us to come inside. I hesitated for a second, for this was unusual, but then quickly did as asked. I picked up my pace, heading that way so I didn't have to suffer any consequence for being late, or just for being in the wrong place at the wrong time. I was a little bit off-balance as the bare bottom of my right foot made contact with the rocks, grass, and concrete slab, but still I made my way to the orphanage.

Once I arrived at the green doorway, I joined the others in wondering what was taking place. We all were a little impatient as we awaited our next command. Once the playground was silent, and everyone was in line, we were all directed inside. Instead of taking a right toward the stairs, where the big white room was, we all went left, toward the cafeteria and kitchen. When we arrived, I sat at the table I was directed to, and saw that every table was clothed with red and white gingham-patterned tablecloths.

I sat in the silence and waited, wondering what this could possibly mean.

CHAPTER TWENTY-ONE

The quiet of the cafeteria was soon interrupted by the echo of high heels making contact with the concrete floor. The sound made me a bit uneasy as it got louder, heading our way. I turned my head toward the entrance with anticipation, along with my brothers and sisters, all of us eagerly awaiting the unknown. Olga stepped through the cafeteria door, and my eyes lit up. A hint of sweet perfume entered the room with her as she smiled, showing her beautiful white teeth. She lit up the atmosphere with her essence, slowly making her way around and giving us hugs and pats on the back.

Behind Olga, a petite lady with a creamy complexion entered with two big white people following suit. They carried a couple of boxes in their hands. Once they entered, they went to the nearest table, putting the boxes down to free their hands and wave at us. Excitement filled the room, for we rarely saw any guests, especially white outsiders. Olga waved her hands toward the ground to get us all quiet. Then she made her announcement.

Someone was getting adopted, and the white couple had a big surprise to give everyone before they went back to America. I knew it had to be me, and I was filled with excitement. I felt like I was being summoned by the grace of a better opportunity. Olga's words replayed in my head while I smiled gleefully at the couple.

The man stepped forward and introduced himself as Steven. He waved and smiled with excitement as the petite, creamy lady interpreted everything he said.

I stared in amazement as I observed my new family. Steven seemed about five-foot-eight in height, and about 200 pounds. He wore a white polo shirt tucked in, making his big stomach pop out. His features were hidden by his gray and black beard, but as I looked into his brown eyes I knew they spoke kindness. Once he finished speaking, the white lady stepped forward, introducing herself as Evelyn. She was a little shorter than Steven, about five-six, and a little bit smaller with blond hair. She wore a white polo shirt that matched her husband's. After she introduced herself, she stepped back and held Steven's hand out of shyness and support. I could tell she was gentle and sweet.

Olga then stepped forward, her black high heels echoing on the concrete floor. A long pause lingered within the room as she built up the suspense to announce who was going to get adopted. I sat on the edge of my seat, ready to get up. It seemed like hours while my heart raced in excitement, and anticipation built as I prepared for my name to be called so I could go home with my new family. I heard some footsteps in the distance, but I tuned them out and focused my attention on Olga. She looked around gleefully at everyone, before her beautiful eyes met mine.

The footsteps in the hallway got louder, and Olga gently turned around, turning her attention away from me. One of my sisters with beautiful blond hair and blue eyes, dressed in a bright white dress, stepped through the entrance door next to a female staff member. I heard Olga announce that Sorina was going to America.

My heart skipped a beat. A ton of bricks had fallen on my heart. My disappointment was immeasurable.

Steven and Evelyn went to Sorina, giving her a hug—embracing her instead of me. I was excited for her, and seeing her adopted made me believe there was hope for me. I was disappointed. I was fearful I had missed my only opportunity to have another life.

Once Steven and Evelyn embraced the new addition to their family, they went to the boxes they had brought with them and revealed the mystery within. They walked around, passing out big green apples to everyone. My disappointment faded as I watched the apples. Steven made his way closer to me, and I put both of my hands out in excitement, for the apple seemed much too big to handle with one hand. I stared at it, wondering how it could get so big, and contemplating how I should eat it. As I pondered, the interpreter stepped forward, translating that we could eat as many apples as our stomachs desired.

I bit into the apple and started to devour it, biting every which way, and already anticipating my next one. As I ate, the translator assured us that there was a plethora of apples left. I finished my first one, barely chewing it, and waited eagerly for the second one, hoping the extra box was still full. Steven made his way to me again as I raised my hand for another one. As he handed it over, I realized the apple he was giving me was even bigger than the first one. I looked at it in awe, wondering what the secret was to getting them so big. I knew this opportunity was rare. I stared at it for a moment, then bit into its green, shiny coat, accepting my second challenge. I devoured every bit of it, besides the core, and was fully satisfied.

Olga asked if we were ready to go outside to say our goodbyes. As we made our way outside, I dreaded my sister and her new family actually leaving. Sorina and her new family got into the yellow Lada automobile, shutting the doors as my siblings and I surrounded the vehicle. We all stared at it in hopes the family would change their mind and visit with us some more. However, the car started up, and I could smell the fumes from the exhaust while Olga told us all to step back for safety. We did as we were asked, watching the back of the car. While it started moving toward the open gates, Sorina turned around in the backseat and waved through the back window. As she waved goodbye, this reality dawned on us, and we chased after the vehicle, trying to keep the dream alive—the dream which we could not have that had come true for her.

CHAPTER TWENTY-TWO

The yellow Lada soon made its way through the green gate and turned right, making all of us stop in our tracks. We listened to the latch on the base of the gate scrape against the driveway as it closed. I lingered, staring through the cracks in the gate as my siblings scattered, sprinting to the swing set. As the car moved out of sight, I stood wondering why it wasn't me. Why couldn't I have been the one adopted by the nice American couple? Finally, dejectedly, I turned around and saw Olga a short distance away, walking back into the orphanage. In my mind I rehearsed the words she had spoken to me. "You're going to be adopted." Somehow, hearing the words, even in my mind, seemed to decrease the fear of torment.

I knew there was nothing I could do as Olga moved inside, so I decided to run east, down the concrete path, to distract myself from my disappointment. I remember the feeling of my bare right foot coming in contact with the pavement as I made my way to the playground, past a bed of blooming pansies. Somehow their beautiful colors seemed a little out of place surrounded by so much that was not beautiful.

My gaze turned to the swing set in hopes of finding one swing free, but—no surprise—all were taken.

I sat next to the concrete path, near a patch of dirt, and started to play with my siblings to pass the time. The dirt was dry, so we could not build with much height, which was disappointing. However, a solution was soon found, as one of my brothers stood and started emptying his bladder on the pile of dirt, to make it moist. Once he finished, I stood and released what little bit I had, and then started digging with the rest of my siblings to pile the dirt as high as we could. I could smell the urine as I grabbed clumps of dirt and tried to compact them to get them formed.

As soon as I patted the dirt I smelled the hint of sweet perfume intermixing with the foul scent of urine on my hands. I gazed up at the orphanage, wondering if the smell had come from there, even though I had seen Olga going inside. As I looked up, though, there in distance, halfway up the concrete path, stood Olga. She was watching me and my siblings at play with a smile on her face. Behind her stood Costin and the lanky man with gray hair, holding two small tires I had never seen before.

As we stared at Olga with anticipation, she waved us all over, grabbing one of the tires from the lanky man. She put it down on the concrete path, and started rolling it ever so slowly, while trying to hold it in balance, before grabbing me and one of the others, encouraging us to "give it a try."

I gleefully accepted the offer and steadied the tire with my dominant left hand, just as I saw her do. I started rolling the tire, and the joy of a new adventure soon filled me as Olga clapped and cheered us on. The swings soon emptied, when those kids heard the sound of our laughter at our new game. They came closer, gathering around, much like a pack of curious wolves. They wanted to see the hype about the new tires and our new game.

We tried to see who could make it first to the black iron gate, rolling the tire. Halfway through, my clumsiness got the best of me, and my tire fell down. I stepped toward the sideline, accepting my defeat, as Olga encouraged others to give it a try. As I awaited my next turn with anticipation, I listened to the cheerful noise taking place and observed my environment. The swing sets sat silent, and the shuffle of many feet on the sidelines soon trampled the piles of dirt castles we built, as another round of tire races began.

CHAPTER TWENTY-THREE

The excitement of this new game echoed in my siblings' voices as each individual child anticipated their turn with the tire. I knew it would be a while before my next turn, so I decided to venture out among the grass. I headed toward the swing set, since there was no one there. Along the way, I noticed a yellow piece of plastic on the ground that no doubt caught my attention because of its appealing brightness. Once I arrived at the mysterious piece, I looked around to make sure it didn't belong to anyone, and then I reached down to examine my new commodity. I figured out it was half of a plastic eggshell, the sort that Olga gave us treats in—and the sort the staff took away from us when we were alone in their presence. I looked around once more, placed the object in the pocket of my overalls, and headed toward the swing set as if nothing had happened, trying to be discreet so the half egg shell could remain mine.

The atmosphere of the playground was still filled with excitement as I made my way to the swing set and started swinging alone. After a moment, as I sat there observing my siblings, solace settled over me. Costin and the lanky man were heading toward the back of the orphanage, where there sat two big cages surrounded with boards. I was watching and wondering what they were doing when Jula called my name, telling me it was my turn to race next.

As I headed toward the concrete path, I searched for Olga, hoping to impress her. She was gone; her presence and her sweet perfume no longer lingering near our play. Regardless, I balanced the tire once more, adrenaline running through me. My brother Luca was to the right of me. He was about four feet in height, with blond, buzzed hair. He uniquely had one blue eye and one brown eye. He gazed at me with determination. Jula counted down from three as the anticipation mounted. Then, we heard the word "Merge!" and the race began.

I took off, trying to balance the tire with my left hand. My right foot hurt from pounding on the concrete path, but I could hear Luca's tire just seconds behind mine, and I blocked out the pain and pushed harder.

I had almost reached the iron gates, but I was afraid to glance back, for I knew the race was close. I arrived at the black iron gates first. Luca's tire rolled into the black gate seconds behind mine. The crowd went wild on the sidelines. I gazed into Luca's eyes and smiled, with a nod to let him know that he did a great job. Jula came and challenged me to race next. My right foot throbbed from the concrete path, but I accepted the offer and made my way back to the starting line.

I stood there, ready to go. Jula threw a curveball, though, when he informed me we both must put a rock in our tires and race down toward the black gate. If the rock flew out of the tire before the finish line, I would lose—or, if I reached the gate, even with my rock in place, second instead of first. I smiled as I accepted this twist on the original challenge.

Jula handed me a small, rough, gray rock. I placed it in my tire and heard it thump into the rubber ever so gently. Meanwhile, one of our brothers started the countdown. I focused, tensed. I then heard the call "Merge!" once more and took off. I felt the sole of my right foot slamming against the concrete. Regardless of the pain, I tried to pick up speed. I could hear my rock tumbling furiously in my tire. Then suddenly, the noise ceased, and out of the left corner of my eye I saw my rock fling out.

Frustrated, I stopped in my tracks, releasing the tire. It kept rolling a few feet in front of me before collapsing. I accepted my defeat as Jula made his way to the black wrought-iron gate. My siblings cheered him on. Others were already making their way toward my fallen tire in hope of getting a chance to win the game.

CHAPTER TWENTY-FOUR

I faded back to the sidelines, hoping for my next turn, but time passed slowly. My stomach started to cramp. I did not want to go to the bathroom and risk missing my turn, so I ignored the pain by trying to figure out what I could get into in the meantime to keep myself occupied. I looked behind me and saw the swing sets were empty. I contemplated whether I should get on one; that rapid movement might not ease my stomach.

I'd turned back around to face the races once more, when out of the corner of my eye I spotted a couple of my siblings climbing on the wrought-iron fence where the Catholic church stood. I watched them hop over to the other side without hesitation, disappearing out of my sight. Curiosity about where they went soon got the best of me, so I headed toward the black iron gate and followed suit behind them, the cheers of my other siblings echoing from the tire game sideline, though they weren't for me.

I quickly climbed the fence and eased myself over the top, careful not to impale myself on the sharp black spikes. Once I was clear, I dropped on the other side and gazed around, taking in the unfamiliar territory. The church was huge, with old wooden doors in the front and concrete paving stones surrounding it. I decided to make my way to the right, creeping alongside the church wall ever so cautiously.

Midway, a strong, foul smell started to fill my nostrils, making me hesitate about whether I should keep moving. The cheers from the orphanage had faded into the background, while the sound of insects buzzing behind the church increased with every step I took. I soon came to a dead end and took a few seconds to calm my nerves as my heart beat rapidly. Then I peeked behind the church.

I gazed in amazement as the foul stink overwhelmed me, for along the whole back side of the church lay nothing but feces. Flies swarmed in the air, and my two siblings were squatting, emptying their bowels. My nervousness slowly subsided and I soon followed suit, undoing my overalls. As I squatted amid the swarm of flies and emptied my bowels my pain subsided. In truth, I was now excited to have discovered this territory.

Once I'd finished what Mother Nature intended, I looked around to see if I could find a leaf to wipe myself with, but there seemed to be no foliage at my disposal. So, I had no choice but to go with what was available. I reached my left hand behind me and wiped. My left hand was now covered with feces. I needed a way to wipe it clean but didn't see anything that would work for this purpose. As I contemplated what I should do next, one of my brothers turned around and smeared the feces that remained on his hand on the wall of the church building.

I don't think I would have ever thought of such an action on my own. Yet I looked at the wall, and could see the dried feces of those who had been there before me. It almost blended in with whatever paint had been used on the building, uncountable years before. So, having witnessed the action of my brothers, I followed suit and wiped my filthy hand on the church wall. The texture of the wall was coarse. The filth on my hand came off easily because of it.

After I finished my business, I walked forward, still squatting, listening to the metal clamps of my overall straps scraping against the ground as I inched clear of the defecation. Once clear, I stood and pulled up my overall straps, feeling much more at ease. I started my way back toward the front of the church. From there, I moved on toward the black wrought-iron gate. I could hear my siblings' cheers increase in intensity.

I jumped back over the fence and quietly faded back into the sidelines, hoping I hadn't missed my turn. I could hear the tires rolling as two of my siblings raced past, making their way toward the gate. I cheered them on and waited for my name to be called. Time seemed to creep by and I became antsy, thinking perhaps I'd missed my turn after all.

I decided again to leave the sidelines, and headed this time toward the open fields to entertain myself. I gazed up at the sky as I moved toward the swings, trying to guess how much time we had left outside, based on the placement of the sun and its natural light.

I wished for the sun to be merciful as I sat on the empty swing set. Once I was seated comfortably, I grabbed the rusty chains and listened to them chime as I started to propel myself. The smell of feces from my left hand intensified as the velocity of my movement back and forth increased. Regardless of the smell, I looked toward the sky. Butterflies in my stomach moved rapidly while gravity started to take over. I started to become a little lightheaded from moving so rapidly while staring into the blue sky, so I shifted my gaze back forward, toward the open field, hoping to regain my equilibrium.

As I looked straight ahead, I noticed Costin was opening the two cages surrounded by boards. I seized the moment and stopped the slowing swing. My feet were solid on the ground, and my curiosity about the cages and what Costin was actually doing got the best of me. Suddenly, two big black and brown German shepherds started to make their way out, heading our way at full speed. I panicked and screamed, in hopes of alerting the others. The barking of the dogs grew loud, angry, and agitated; they were clearly on a mission.

Fear raged within me as one dog ran straight toward me. I turned around and moved toward the swing I had abandoned just moments before. Looking for a place of safety, the idea of climbing on top of the swing set hit me. Acting with intent, I climbed my way to the top, holding on with all the strength I had.

Once I had a good grip on the swing set's top bar and I felt safe, I looked out to watch my siblings running away. Their fearful screams filled the air as one of the dogs chased them, while the other lingered below me with its sharp white teeth bared, barking with fury.

CHAPTER TWENTY-FIVE

Fear coursed through my body. My heart pounded. The dog's barking paralyzed me. I held on to the top of the swing set with all the strength I could muster, hoping I would not fall to the lingering dog. The sun was dropping, day turning to dusk. My body became weary as time passed. I wondered if this was where I would stay for the rest of the night.

Soon, out of the corner of my eye, I saw a figure coming toward me. I recognized his black curly hair and his stocky frame; it was Costin. He made his way over and gazed up at me with a smile. His piercing eyes met mine with a sly hint of a smile. He whistled, ever so gently, patting his thigh. The German shepherd ceased its barking, turned around, and went to Costin without any sign of its previously displayed aggression. Costin reached down to pat the dog and they both headed back to the cages as if nothing had happened.

I hung there, stunned and afraid to get down, for I knew that one more dog was lingering in the field, somewhere out of sight. After a few minutes passed, I decided to make my way down from the top of the swing set, hoping to find shelter before the other dog could find me. I spotted the other German shepherd next to the lanky white man across the field as they headed back toward the cages. The sight of them made me halt in my tracks. The dog turned my way, making eye contact as if ready to sprint at me. I froze, my heart beating rapidly in fear, as I stared into its eyes, wondering if I should bolt and make my way back up to safety.

The lanky man stared in my direction, sensing the dog's ambition. However, he commanded the dog to make his way back to where Costin stood. Fear and doubt still burned in the forefront of my thoughts, so I decided to stay halfway between the swing set and the building as I watched both dogs make their way back to their cages. After a few moments, my fear subsided, and I started to make my way back to the orphanage.

Along the way, I heard a faint female voice yell from the south end of the orphanage that it was time for dinner. I picked up my pace. I could feel my right foot aching with every stride. Along the way, my other siblings popped out of their hiding places and joined in, running to the safety of the building. They, too, had been frightened by the threat of being attacked by a German shepherd.

Inside, we made our way to the cafeteria. The tables remained the same, with the red and white gingham-patterned plastic tablecloths. It made me wonder what the special occasion was, as we shuffled down the line to get our dinner at the kitchen window. When I arrived at the window to receive my food, I stared into the rusty bowl in amazement, for in it was a yellow, grainy substance I had never seen before. Without hesitation, I took it, and sat as commanded. I then reached for the spoon in front of me, and started to dig in with anticipation and wonder, placing the substance on my tongue. I didn't care for the flavor of it, but I ate every bite in hopes it would fill my hunger.

After I scarfed it down, I pushed the bowl aside, and listened to the scraping of the other children's spoons, awaiting our next instruction. The hallway soon was filled with a tapping sound of footsteps that echoed among the other chaos. Excitement filled me, anticipation for the sight of Olga. I took a deep breath, ready to smell the hint of her sweetness. However, as the tapping came closer, there was no accompanying scent. I turned toward the doorway, cheerfully still, wondering who might come through, when an elderly man I had never seen entered.

He was possibly five-feet, six-inches in height, with a belly that was much bigger than his height could handle. He wore light brown pants and a dark brown sweater that had holes on the left side of the sleeve. His short, salt-and-pepper hair was covered with a wool-blend ivy cap that was striped, black, and light brown. We all looked at him as he stood in the doorway. He held six large woven sacks in his hand. He stared back at us without even the slightest smile.

CHAPTER TWENTY-SIX

The scraping of spoons ceased as the elderly man slowly made his way around the room. I watched him giving sacks to various children he seemed to pick out from the rest of the group. A little fear arose within me but I was curious, too, as he turned toward our table holding two sacks in his hand. I sat in silence as he looked into my brown eyes. After a long silence, he handed me a bag and muttered with his raspy voice to follow him. The metal chair scraped behind me as I pushed it back to stand and follow him as he had commanded.

At his instruction, each child who had been given a sack made our way outside. I gazed up at the darkening sky. Just a little light still remained, and I wondered what our purpose was as we headed to the open field. When we neared the swing set, he told us his name was Gheorghe. Then he simply instructed all of us to fill the sacks with grass. While I certainly didn't understand the purpose of such a command, I did as he asked and ventured to the most prevalent spot where grass grew.

I fell on my knees and went straight to work. I could hear the ripping of the grass as I reached down with both fists and began filling the sack, intent on impressing the old man. My knees started to hurt after the sack was halfway full, but I blocked out the pain. I could feel the dirt compacting beneath my fingernails with every fistful of green grass I grabbed. I heard the rustling of footsteps near me and smelled the aroma of the grass being released with every tear.

I shifted slightly to the right, hoping to get a better grip, when I saw a pair of brown, worn pants facing me. I moved my arms rapidly without looking up so I would not disappoint my master. Without hesitation, Gheorghe grabbed my sack. I looked up, and Gheorghe was smiling at me, showing me his unpolished teeth as he handed me another empty bag. I did as I was told and started tearing up the grass around me again as darkness fell. My arms' stamina slowly began to give out, but regardless, I did my best to fill the second sack to the brim. My work went more slowly than it had the first time, as my knees started to hurt, to the point where I couldn't block out the pain. Nonetheless, I finished my task.

Once my second bag was full, Gheorghe's raspy voice called for each of us to grab the sacks we had filled and follow him. I grabbed my sack with both hands. It was hard to steady myself and keep my balance, for the sack was bigger than I was. I took a moment to catch my breath, then I followed right behind Gheorghe to where his horse and wagon waited by the big green gate. I placed my sacks in the back of the wagon where I smelled horse manure.

After all the sacks were loaded, I hopped off the wagon. Gheorghe went to the front of the wagon and muttered something under his breath as he rustled through his belongings, looking for something. Once he found what he was looking for, he hopped off the wagon, holding an old white handkerchief filled with something. Slowly, he started to make his way back to us.

CHAPTER TWENTY-SEVEN

I waited eagerly as Gheorghe held the handkerchief in one hand while revealing what was inside with the other. It was bread—not just crumbs, but actual pieces of bread. I stared at it, awaiting my turn to get my part of the grub he was passing out. Once he faced my direction, I reached out my hand and received my reward.

I bit into it without hesitation, but quickly realized that it was much too stale. I took a moment and stared at the bread. It had some mold growing on it, and I contemplated how I could soften it. I looked around to see if there was any source of water at my disposal, but of course there was none. I did the best next thing and started to build up my saliva, bringing it to the forefront of my palate and biting into the bread once more, chewing it with all the strength I had to satisfy my hunger. My jaw muscles ached with every bite. Regardless, I didn't give up until I'd eaten every morsel.

Once everyone had finished their snacks, Gheorghe took us inside. He led us upstairs and guided each of us to our own beds as our other siblings were already sleeping. When it came to my turn to follow him, he led me back to the second furthest room on the right, where it was very dark. As we arrived at our destination, he turned on the light, waking some of my siblings. He pointed to an empty bed and told me that was where I would be sleeping. I did as he asked and headed to the scratched-up wooden bed, taking off my shoes as Gheorghe watched me. I then took off my overalls and listened to the metal clasps hitting the floor. I realized that I still had my yellow plastic treasure hidden in the overalls. I panicked, afraid I might not get it if I didn't retrieve it now.

I slowly reached in my left pocket before taking off my overalls. I got the treasure in my hand, then quickly tossed it underneath the bed as I pulled them completely off. Once my gift from Olga was secure, I tossed the rest of my clothes into the middle of the room before hopping into bed as if I had nothing to hide. Once I was in bed and secure, Gheorghe started heading toward my bed. A slight panic arose in me.

I watched him intently as he bent over—his pot-belly got in the way—and grabbed my clothes off the floor before heading out and turning off the lights. Darkness filled the room once more. I exhaled a sigh of relief at dodging any punishment.

As I lay there in my bed, my uneasiness over the darkness of the room began to increase. I started blinking my eyes rapidly, and soon my vision adjusted to what little light was coming in from the orphanage's middle bedrooms. I relaxed, placed my thumb in my mouth, and began rocking my head back and forth to become dizzy enough to pass out. However, my mouth soon became parched, and I could feel that my bladder was full, which made me feel such unease that I couldn't fall asleep. I lay there, trying to figure out whether I should get up and head toward the bin in the middle of the room, to empty my bladder. The thought of satisfying my thirst also burned in the forefront of my mind.

Then I got the idea of doing both of them at once. I got up and reached underneath my bed, hoping to find the half plastic eggshell that Olga had given me. After a few moments of groping in the darkness, I felt the plastic piece in my hand and quickly hopped back into my bed, where I felt most secure. Once I was comfortably back in my bed, I started to empty my bladder within the plastic egg, then drink my own urine to quench my thirst. The flavor was robust and unsatisfying, but I repeated the process once more to moisten my parched mouth.

I could barely get the second round down as the pungent urine hit my taste buds; nonetheless, I did what I had to, before emptying the remains of my bladder on my bed. After I was at ease and fully satisfied, I started to rock my head back and forth on my pillow viciously, while the flavor of my urine lingered in my palate. At last I became lightheaded and drifted into a deep sleep.

CHAPTER TWENTY-EIGHT

The shouts of the staff woke me, and I tuned into the cries of my siblings that echoed from a distance. I checked my underwear as the stench of urine filled my nostrils, but joy filled me, for my urine had dried during the night. I quickly got out of bed as the shouts of the staff made their way closer to our room.

No sooner had I gotten up, than I saw Costin making his way toward me while he and the other young male staff members banged their sticks on the edges of the beds. The smells of urine and feces filled the atmosphere. My heart beat faster with fear. I stood still, and Costin passed by me. The coast was clear; I hadn't suffered any harm.

I relaxed somewhat as a female staff member made her way in and placed the big white sheet in the middle of the room, revealing the clothes within. After she undid the sheet, she gave us all the cue to make our way toward the pile of clothes, and we obeyed, just as we had many times before. I grabbed a yellow turtleneck, a pair of jeans that were a tad too small, and some tennis shoes that were slightly too big, before heading back to my bed to get dressed. When everyone was dressed, we fell in line as commanded and headed downstairs to eat the same breakfast we'd consumed many times before.

Once we'd all finished breakfast, we were led outside, to the big green gate. On the way, I gazed into the sky. The sun was breaking through the clouds, as a gentle, cold breeze blew fitfully. The gate soon opened, and I came back to my reality as I realized we were headed toward the school. As usual, I looked into all of the shops and dreamed once again of having the clothes and bikes displayed in the windows. I soon arrived at the black wrought-iron gates of the school. I dreaded the thought of my classmates' eyes on me; nonetheless, I climbed the stairway. The door was opened, and I walked in, looking down at the scratched wooden floor without making eye contact with anyone, simply wishing I were invisible.

I made my way to a seat in the back, away from the crowd, hoping to avoid the judgment of my peers. I sat down, ready to drift into my own imagination. "Zoltan," Mrs. Andrea called my name, bringing me back to my reality. I heard the classroom erupt with laughter. I was pretty certain something was about to happen that would give my classmates another reason to mock me. However, I still wanted to please the teacher.

I made eye contact with her to see what she needed. She waved me up to the blackboard and instructed me to write a few cursive letters there. I stared at her, not knowing what the letters were, and the class giggled at my obvious ignorance. After a couple of minutes of awkward silence, she took the initiative to write on the board, and I copied the letters she made. Once I'd finished, she gave me a smile and dismissed me back to my seat. I could feel the eyes of my classmates following me as I took my seat.

I sat, gleeful that I did not get punished. I soon drifted back into my own little world, imagining I wore the nice clothes I saw in the store display and rode a red, beautiful bike down the cobblestone road. The bell on Mrs. Andrea's desk startled me, bringing me back from my daydream. It was time for recess.

CHAPTER TWENTY-NINE

The sky was a clear blue; the sun was shining brightly. I sat on the school steps as my classmates played. The pebbles beneath their feet crunched, raising dust as they ran from each other in their game of tag. I sat there, watching them, feeling like a wallflower and wondering what the purpose of their game was. My stomach rumbled. After a few minutes passed, my amusement at watching my classmate ebbed. I sneaked inside, knowing they would not miss me, and headed to the classroom to once again ease my stomach pain from the perpetual hunger with which I lived.

My heart beat rapidly as I went into the classroom to start my treasure hunt, for I knew the consequences that would inevitably follow this excursion. However, my hunger was stronger than my sensibilities.

The first couple of desks had nothing in them. Afraid of being caught, I glanced outside the classroom window to make sure my classmates were still outside. Once I felt safe, knowing they were still playing, I went to a desk in the middle of the room. There, to my surprise, a treasure lay wrapped in clear plastic.

I unwrapped it and looked at the overstuffed sandwich. I had a few bites of it, and I decided to help myself and take a few more bites. My mouth was so full

I could barely chew. I wrapped the sandwich back up, knowing that was wiser than eating it all. I then went to the next desk. There was nothing, and I decided to make my way back downstairs before the class came back. I listened to my instincts, closed the classroom door behind me, and rushed downstairs.

Wiping my mouth clean of evidence, I made my way outside. My nervousness increased as the sun's rays met me, and I sat back down on the school steps. A few minutes went by as I listened to sounds of laughter and the clatter of the pebbles being kicked around. I waited for someone to confront me, to ask where I'd been, but nothing happened.

The teacher soon rang her bell, rounding us up, and she looked straight at me. It was as if she needed to make sure I was counted. After we were all accounted for, we headed upstairs to the classroom and went back to our seats. My mind buzzed with fear while I watched a petite girl in a jean jacket lift her desktop in the middle of the classroom to ensure nothing was missing. After a few long seconds, she closed her desk back up and a sigh of relief overcame me.

I tried to tune in to the teacher talking up front, but my imagination soon got the best of me, and I slowly slipped again into a daydream filled with the things I couldn't have. Suddenly the bell rang louder than before, making me jump. Mrs. Andrea informed us that class was over for the day. I couldn't believe it. I didn't know how to tell time, but I was amazed at how fast the time flew by.

I got up, ran downstairs, full-speed, and made my way outside where the sun still shone brightly. I listened to the pebbles crunch beneath my feet, as I had many times before, and exited into the street, the real world, the world of mystery that fueled my imagination.

CHAPTER THIRTY

Horses trotted along the cobblestone road, pulling the wagons. I walked along the sidewalk, listening to the clip-clop of the horses combined with the roll of wheels on cobblestone. All the while, the smell of horse manure intensified with the sun's rays. I gazed again into the shop windows that displayed clothes, toys, and other goodies. As I took it all in, my stomach growled, reminding me I must get something to eat. There had to be a dumpster or two nearby. However, I would have to move fast to do my "dumpster diving" and be back at the orphanage.

Soon I spotted a large dumpster just a couple of blocks ahead. I picked up speed and made my way toward it. Once I'd arrived, I eyeballed it, trying to guess how full it might be. The lids were closed. Rust had eaten a hole on the side of the metal, so I could peer in, looking for treasured cabbage ends.

To my surprise, as I put my eye to the hole, another human eye met mine from within. I backed up, startled. The dumpster lid popped up, revealing a man and his wife, who both screamed with rage at me. The man pulled out a horse whip and cracked it in my direction. The crack of the whip echoed like thunder behind me as I ran to avoid getting hit.

A few blocks away, I slowed my running and crouched near another dumpster, my heart beating rapidly. I took a few minutes to catch my breath and let my panic subside before I started to make my way back to the orphanage. I was still hungry, yet too afraid to take a chance and look inside this second dumpster. I feared it might be occupied, like the last one, and the second time I might not escape harm.

I slowly made my journey back to the orphanage, the place I called home. Once I arrived at the gates, I stalled for a moment or two, lingering between both universes. When I was ready to face my true reality again, I took a deep breath and knocked on the big green gate. A staff member answered my summons, and I stepped inside as commanded, glancing around in shock. My home was covered in scaffolding. As I looked around, it appeared that some walls of the orphanage were being torn down, while other sections were being restored and painted a beautiful pearl color. I couldn't help staring at the walls and all the work in progress in disbelief. I looked a little closer as the sound of laughter filled the air. Some of my siblings were dancing around a gold Dacia 1304 truck.

The truck had a white cap covering the back of the bed and was parked near the entrance doors of the orphanage. As I glanced at the truck, Olga stepped through the doors of the building. She veered in the direction of my siblings, smiling at all of them with genuine kindness. Her eyes soon met mine, as I, as usual, was mesmerized by her, following her every move. She quickly waved me toward her as my other siblings surrounded her.

Once I made my way there, she smiled at me with her beautiful white teeth; soon her sweet fragrance filled my lungs. Leaning in, she whispered, "I have a big surprise for you." I wondered what it was. I looked around. While my siblings surrounded Olga, laughing, the staff members stayed distant and obedient. I looked at Olga again in hopes of seeing what my surprise was, and she pointed toward the big green gate, which was opening.

A Dacia 1310 automobile drove in, coming toward us. The car parked, and butterflies filled my stomach as two white women stepped out of the vehicle and looked around, observing our environment. I stared at both of them in awe, wondering if they would be my new parents, as Olga headed toward them to introduce herself. I watched both of the ladies intently as they conversed with Olga, knowing they were not local ladies. Random visitors to the orphanage were rare. I was excited at all the reasons I could imagine for these ladies to be visiting.

One of the ladies was skinny with wavy black hair, slightly past her shoulder. She wore spectacles with circular lenses and a black shirt that was small and showed her belly. A Polaroid camera hung from a strap around her neck. She laughed with Olga, while the other lady with her seemed slightly more reserved. The second woman was medium-sized, with short blond hair about shoulder-length. She wore a jean jacket. My siblings and I watched both of them in amazement.

Olga waved me over and introduced me to Ilinca, the one carrying the camera, and Mira, her associate. After introductions were made, and names exchanged, they looked at each other and started speaking a language I couldn't understand. I stood there with Olga, trying to tune in to anything that sounded familiar. Once they had finished talking, they started motioning for all of my siblings to get into a semicircle. Olga looked down at me with her beautiful eyes before stepping aside.

Mira guided me into the middle of the semicircle. An overwhelming joy filled me while I stood there, the black Polaroid camera pointed at me. As I stood there and listened to the camera's click, with each shot the thought of being adopted that day ran through my mind, filling me with even more excitement and anticipation. This was the day; there was no doubt.

Once they'd finished taking the pictures, with me in the center, my siblings broke out of their semicircle pose. Mira and Ilinca headed toward their car and grabbed a small box filled with goodies. As the two ladies headed back our way, we watched them eagerly, wondering what was in the box.

They made their way back with the box. Mira reached into it, revealing small, colorful yarn designs that were given as gifts to everyone. We all accepted them, not knowing what exactly they were, but nonetheless we used our imaginations and played with our gifts. Ilinca took pictures of us as we surrounded the two women in gratitude. After the box was empty, and the sounds of the camera's clicking had ceased, my new "parents" said their goodbyes with some hugs and waves.

As they started walking to their car with the empty box, I stood near them, wondering where they were going without me. Perhaps they were just settling into the vehicle, preparing to wave me over so I could climb in. But the car started. I could smell the exhaust as I watched the two ladies through the windshield, hoping to remind them they were leaving me behind. The car started to move forward, putting more distance between me and my dreams. They made their way to the gate without stopping. I stood in the middle, between my dream and reality, wondering what I had done wrong for my new family to change their minds.

I looked back at Olga while I repeated her words: *You are going to America. You are going to America.* As I stood there, watching the car drive away, I no longer believed it. I had seen the truth, had watched it drive right out of those horrible green gates.

CHAPTER THIRTY-ONE

I listened to the gates close and latch once more, sealing me in my devastating reality. I could smell a hint of Olga's sweet perfume dancing in the wind, yet this time it made me even sadder than the disappearing taillights. I wondered how I had failed to be a suitable choice. I wondered what I could have done better. I wondered what I had said or done that made them drive away without me.

I listened to my siblings running around, laughing while they played with their new toys. I turned around to face my solace once more, to remind myself of Olga's words. Except this time, when I turned around, Olga had already gone back in.

Luca called my name from a distance. He waved me over to where he was standing, in the alleyway on the west side of the orphanage, along the concrete wall that was almost hugging our home. I straightened my shoulders, took a deep breath, and got myself together, determined to hide my disappointment and distract my own mind from its disillusion. I stared into his eyes—as I mentioned before, one blue and the other brown—wondering why he was standing there. He pointed at the ground, as if he had read my mind, and asked if I could help him pick up some rocks. However, he was very specific in his request.

He did not want just any rocks. He wanted pairs, one that was clear and another that was gray.

I look at him a little oddly for a second as he showed me his findings, then I agreed to the task and bent down to look for similar pairs of rocks as the ones in his hand. The rocks he asked for were rare, few and far between, but I looked for them intently as an array of other rocks crunched beneath my feet.

Luca soon spoke, muttering to me very faintly, "If you go to America, they will cut you open and sell your organs." I stood there appalled, wondering how he might have known I was going to America, as the unsettling thought of what he just said ran through my mind. Suddenly, from a distance, I heard Costin and another young male staff member yelling for all of us to line up and head inside. Their words caused the laughter and excitement from my siblings to cease. I looked at Luca quizzically, handing him the couple of sets of rocks I had collected. Then we turned around to head to the orphanage.

We made our way to the entrance door as the playground became silent. The line followed Costin inside while the other male staff member with the curly black hair and chiseled features corralled us from behind as we made our way upstairs. An uneasy feeling of fear and frustration settled within me. The ritual was now my reality, and it was disheartening. Once we arrived at our destination, I stood at the big white door, as I had many times before, and listened to it squeak open.

Fear ran down my spine. I took a few deep breaths to prepare myself for what was to come. However, once I made my way inside, I was surprised. Excitement filled me, making my heart pound with anticipation.

CHAPTER THIRTY-TWO

I blinked my eyes rapidly, as if in a dream. I stared, and gazed around in awe at the new colors that invited us in. The fireplace was still at a forty-five-degree angle, banked in the back-left corner, but everything else was brand-new. The walls were a nice cream color, with no holes in them, and the smell of fresh paint filled the atmosphere. The benches were no longer dark wood with bite marks or scratches. Instead, metal benches were painted with a bright array of colors: red, yellow, lime green, Turkish blue, and hot pink were in place, making the room feel brighter and more welcoming.

In the center, up front, was the most fascinating thing yet. It was an old-school TV that sat in a white, wall-mounted box. There was constant static in the background of the screen no matter what show was being played. Regardless, I stared at the new-found technology in awe, for I had never seen such a thing. As I stood there, looking around at my new environment, Costin made his way up front and turned off the TV, making the sound of the static come to an end. The other male staff were rounding the rest of my siblings up into the big white room.

After we were all corralled inside, Costin started commanding each of us to take a seat, one by one. When it came to my turn, I looked up at Costin, awaiting my command. He pointed to the back-left side where the Turkish blue bench sat. I did as he asked and made my way toward the back, the smell of his sweat, intermixed with the fresh paint, filling my nostrils. Once everyone was seated, the big white doors closed with a bang, making me jump, as we all sat in silence anticipating the unexpected. Within the eerie silence, I tuned in to the footsteps of both male staff members. The sound echoed ever so gently on the refurbished wooden floor as each of them made their way opposite one another.

The trepidation in the room intensified. Costin went to the TV. He reached behind it, within the white wooden box, pulling out a very thin twig with foliage still on it. As I lay my eyes on the small stick, I started rocking back and forth ever so slowly, accepting my fate, while the other male staff members lingered behind me, near the fireplace. I dared not turn around to see what he was doing behind me, until I heard the scraping of the metal base by the fireplace shift. I was tempted to look, yet I dared not move. Costin and his cohort prowled the aisleway, choosing their next prey.

CHAPTER THIRTY-THREE

I rocked myself back and forth, tuning my ears not to miss the frightening sounds that were so frequently the background of my life. I was trying valiantly to keep calm. Perhaps this day would be different; it wasn't.

The room was filled with silence as both men carried the same weapon of choice—a thin but sturdy branch from a nearby tree—behind their backs. The only sound I could hear was the gentle scratching as the foliage on the sticks dragged behind them on the floor of the aisle. Their treads got louder as they made their way closer to the back where I sat, making me feel uneasy. I kept my guard up, listening to the faint sounds of their steps as they made another loop around, like some strange form of click-by-click, step-by-step clockwork.

I listened as their strides got louder and louder once again. Regardless of how many times I heard the sounds of their tracks increase and decrease, the writhing fear within me never ceased to intensify as they walked away, then came closer again.

Abruptly, the big white door creaked open, filling the room with even more light, and the staff members' strides came to a quick halt. A sweet, familiar fragrance intermixed with the fresh paint. I dared not look behind me to confirm my hopes. Instead, I did what I knew best, and continued to sit very still, staring straight ahead.

In the reflection of the TV screen, I was able to see the person standing in the doorway. Olga's familiar, friendly voice filled the silence, and I turned around triumphantly with my other siblings as she walked in, asking all of us what we thought about our newly renovated room. We all smiled and chimed in at once as the room filled with our voices, telling her how much we loved it. She smiled, walking up the aisle in her black high heels. I watched her; she dominated the room while she gazed at the two staff members with her beautiful smile. The men smiled back at her while they hid their weapons behind their backs, underneath their T-shirts.

I wanted to scream, to yell about the evil among us, but I was much too afraid. The only thing I could do was hope Olga would see the true reality of what was taking place as she made her way around, interacting with each of us. I could smell her sweet perfume as she came closer. Once she was near, I stared into her beautiful hazel eyes, trying to look back and forth discreetly between her and the staff members, to possibly let her know what was happening. However, it seemed as if she had no clue what I was doing. I wondered whether I should whisper to her and let her know what was taking place, but she moved to greet my other siblings before I could figure out a way to convey my pain.

I sat there, frustrated at myself, as I tried to envision what I could do next to get her attention. Her kind presence engulfed the atmosphere, but the fear of getting punished also dominated my mind. I then heard her voice echo among the collateral sounds. She was saying goodbye, and I knew I did not have much time to act.

So it was that, in the moment, as she turned around, facing the big white doors, I started rocking back and forth viciously and tried to discreetly make some noises to get her attention. But the panic within me was too great. I tried to quell my distress, listening to her high heels collide with the wooden floor as she slowly headed toward the exit.

That's when a faint, broken squeak came out of me. I knew I needed to get louder as she neared the exit, but the louder my voice echoed, the fainter her steps became, until it was too late.

CHAPTER THIRTY-FOUR

I hoped Olga had heard my cries, but my worst fear was fulfilled as the doors closed behind her once again. Olga had not heard me; the others had.

I ceased my rocking back and forth. Both male chaperones conspired behind us for a moment. Then an uncanny silence was filled with the familiar echo of Costin and the other male staff member's footsteps as they plodded around us. I could feel their presence as one of them loitered close behind me. I tried to stand still and not make any noise as panic raged within me.

Without warning, pain emerged from the crown of my head, and I screamed, my voice filling the quiet of the room as I was thrown to the floor by my hair. After my squall, I tried to catch my breath, as I was dragged to the back of the room. I panicked, the smell of perspiration filling my nostrils. In the back of the room, I lay on the floor, trying to numb the twinge of pain in my head. I willed myself to ignore the pain, to stop crying.

The metal base of the fireplace was angled uncomfortably against my back, but there was no comfort to be found. The pain on my crown increased once more as Costin pulled me up by my hair, facing me toward the brick fireplace on my knees. He yanked both my arms up, and raised them as high as they could go above my head. I could feel my head throb with every heartbeat as I ceased my whimpering. My knees started to feel a slight pain from the metal hearth. I stayed still, to get myself together, but I was too uncomfortable. I shifted my weight, in hope of getting some reprieve, my arms still raised high.

Out of the corner of my eye, I spotted a few green leaves fluttering down and hitting the floor as Costin stripped the foliage off his branch. I looked straight ahead at the brick wall, trying to ignore what I knew I was about to endure, as the first sting rippled through my back. With each strike, the pain increased, as the switch came down with full force on my upper thighs. I knew I could not hide my pain for long. However, I was determined to stay quiet as long as I could, listening to the stick whoosh through the air with every lash. I no longer cared about trying to overcome the pain; instead, I invited it in.

With every *whack,* anger began to boil up from within me. I took a deep breath. The smells of fresh paint and sweat lingered around me. I realized I was within the furnace of hell itself. They hadn't been tearing the orphanage down; they had been painting it. The colors might have changed around me, but the color did very little to disguise my own torture chamber.

I no longer sought a rescuer. Rather, I prayed to find quiet as I felt another strike across my back.

CHAPTER THIRTY-FIVE

With my arms above my head I clenched my fists tighter with every swinging whack as the switch came in contact with my back and lower thighs. I tried to master the pain, though I could barely contain it. *This is just too hard for me to handle,* I thought, as the stick whooshed through the air, increasing its momentum with every strike.

Tears started to well up in my eyes. Still, I refused to even mutter, much less cry out. The thought of accepting such a defeat seeped into my mind. My entire body seemed to ache with the pain, yet I held myself still, hoping to limit the extent of my punishment. I was in a daze, though I could still feel the intense burning radiate across my back and thighs with every blow. My teeth ground together as I held my emotions in.

Then, abruptly, the sound of the thin stick whooshing through the air ceased. I was on the verge of breaking, while I tried to stay strong and remain upright. Still, I soon became weak. I could feel my arms and upper body lowering, cringing from the blows to find some reprieve. None was found, for Costin yanked me back upright by my arms.

Suddenly, a loud female cry erupted directly behind me. As I stared at the brick wall, the screaming got louder. Soon a loud thump followed, as if the girl's body hit the wooden floor. I wanted to turn around to see the commotion, but my body ached and I was much too afraid of further punishment.

My sister howled as she was dragged to the center of the room. Then came the familiar whooshing of sticks coming in contact with her body, making her holler even louder than before. I tried to block out her cries, but the more I tried, the more ear-splitting they became. I closed my eyes, telling myself that this was all a nightmare, but the brutal reality of the girl's screams told me otherwise.

A sudden, faint knock at the door to my left sounded amid the howls and crying, but the staff didn't hear it. I prayed it was Olga, here to catch them in the act. The right far door opened, making the light flood in from outside. I looked that way in anticipation and hope. However, it was a female staff member, popping her head in and informing us that it was time for dinner, ignoring what she might have interrupted.

Both of the male chaperones ceased their strikes against my sister and began yelling at all of us to get in line. I acted quickly, lowering my arms and sighing at my reprieve. My arms were weak and limp, flopping around like useless skin bereft of bones. My back and thighs ached. I managed to stand up gradually and rub my knees, feeling the pattern from the fireplace's metal base indented in them. I slowly pulled myself together. Once I could muster the strength to stand fully, I turned around to get in line.

There, in the middle of the floor, lay a tall, lanky female with dark brown hair. Her eyes were red and swollen, and she wore a tight pink shirt a little too small for her frame. She propped herself up with both of her hands and I gazed at her in amazement, for on her left hand was an extra thumb. I had never seen that before. I kept my eyes on her as I made my way to the line, and I watched her sniffling, trying to catch her breath. I could see the snot running down her nose, as she looked around, still appalled at what had just taken place.

Costin, from the front of the line, started to make his way toward her. He grabbed her by the hair without mercy, and yanked her up off the floor. She screamed with agony and I looked away, staring straight ahead, as she was lugged to the back of the line a few feet behind me. I tried to make sense of his cruelty as I stood there, but I could not understand such a punishment, no matter how I tried to justify it in my head.

As Costin made his way back up front, he dropped a chunk of the girl's hair from his hand.

CHAPTER THIRTY-SIX

In the cafeteria, I did my best to maneuver my spoon and scoop up the mingled bread and water. I could manage only a couple of bites before I felt exhausted. I put my spoon down and took a short break, trying to regain what little strength I had in my arms. I sat listening to my siblings' spoons scraping against their rusty metal bowls, all of them out of sync, each eating faster than the one sitting next to them.

As I gazed around, I noticed the staff member with the curly black hair and chiseled features get out of his seat and start walking toward the back of the cafeteria, where a couple of my brothers sat next to the big fireplace, eating. I watched the staff member intently as he made his way to the back, while both of my brothers stared at him, wondering what they might have done. They were twins and had short, black, shiny hair and brown, creamy complexions. One of them had a bald patch on the left side of his head. I could feel the eerie unease both of my siblings felt as the male chaperone approached their table and grinned, taunting them, before grabbing one of the brothers' hands, making him drop his spoon. I could see the fear in his eyes as he started to writhe around in his chair to get away from the torment. He started to shout, and some of my other siblings' spoons came to a halt as they turned toward the source of the cry.

My brother bucked around, trying to resist the chaperone's grip on his right hand. I watched as the staff member tried to pull apart the boy's middle finger and ring finger, which had been fused together since birth. My brother screamed and flailed, finally yanking his arm back as he cried for mercy. The staff member only laughed and slapped him across the face, almost making him fall out of his seat. All I could do was sit and hope I would not be next as the male chaperone walked away from the table, chuckling to himself.

Costin chimed in, yelling from the opposite side of the cafeteria for all of us to get in line. I glanced into my rusty bowl, which still had a lot of food in it. I knew I could not eat my food fast enough, and feared further punishment if I did not follow orders.

All around me, chairs scraped on the concrete floor as my siblings stood up to get in line. I struggled to get out of my seat, but managed to slowly rise and get in line. Knowing my hunger was the least of my worries, I followed as the chaperones corralled us back upstairs.

CHAPTER THIRTY-SEVEN

As I walked up the stairs, looking down at the torn red and white carpet, I could always hear the sound of the carpet-keeper rods colliding within the metal insert on each stair step. With every step one of us took, there was that familiar click-clack sound. Some things never changed; this background sound was one of them.

My heart pounded, my body ached, and I dreaded what was to come as we made our way into the hallway where the big white room sat to the right of us. My stomach growled as we were commanded to halt. Costin stood in front of the line, and the other male chaperone lingered behind us. We stood still in front of the big white doors, while the smell of cigarettes, fresh paint, and coffee mingled in the air. A couple of female chaperones sat in their chairs to the left of us, smoking and drinking their coffee in the hallway.

I dreaded the unknown, and a mortal fear grew within me, as Costin broke away from the front of the line. I watched him as he veered toward the female chaperones, asking for a cigarette from the red and white pack sitting on the table between them. I stood still, observing them from midway back in the line, and listened as they conversed. Costin took a cigarette, lighting it with a see-through lighter that was filled halfway with lighter fluid. As the flame came closer to his face, I could see it dance in the reflection of his dark brown pupils. The tip of the cigarette soon became cherry red as he took a puff, before letting the smoke escape his mouth and nostrils, as if he were a dragon, ruthless and unmerciful. I quailed at what was to come next in the big white room as Costin tossed the lighter back to the center of the table and headed to the front of the line.

I turned my head to the right, ready to move to the big white room, but to my surprise Costin moved us forward, toward the bedrooms. My body ached as we passed the big white doors and entered into the center of the bedrooms, the female chaperones followed behind us. I was so excited that rest was soon to come. The smell of urine and feces intermixed with the odor of cigarettes burning, and a hint of coffee. We stood there while Costin told each of us what part of the bedrooms we would sleep in. The female chaperones scattered, one left and the other right, as the line kept creeping up. I stood patiently, hoping I would be assigned a room with even a halo of the light.

The line crept along, but when it came to my turn my wishful thinking evaporated, for Costin directed me toward the far back-right room, where nothing but darkness beckoned.

CHAPTER THIRTY-EIGHT

My back and thighs ached, and I dreaded sleeping in the dark, but even still I moved to the right and did as asked, passing through other bedrooms along the way that had all their beds filled. When I arrived at my destination, a female staff member with short, messy, blond hair greeted me with a sour face. She smelled of cigarettes and stale smoke. The lines in her face showed youth was escaping her. She pointed to a bed on the right, telling me that was where I would sleep. Without hesitation, I nodded and walked to my bed before sitting on the edge of it. I could smell the strong stench of old urine lingering near me as I pulled my arms through the yellow turtleneck to get undressed.

As I tried to pull the turtleneck off, my head got stuck in the neck canal. I struggled for a couple of minutes, trying to get it off, mustering all of my leverage. However, my body ached, and I couldn't do it. I started to panic that I would never get it off. I felt a tugging that was not of my strength. I couldn't see what was going on, and fear rose in me as I heard the female staff member telling me to stay still, while she grabbed what loose part of the shirt she could and pulled on it. I could feel the hairs near the back of my neckline scream with pain as she tugged with all her strength before finally getting it off of me.

I stood in a daze while the chaperone turned around and tossed the turtleneck into the middle of the dirty pile with the other clothes, before heading back to the doorway. I was so thankful the shirt came off as I sat back down on the edge of the bed. I let out a sigh of relief and lifted my right foot to remove my shoes and short jeans. After I got undressed down to my underwear, I tossed my dirty garments and shoes into the center. All I could think about was wanting to lie down.

As I pulled my covers back, the stench of urine that had seemed to linger hit me head-on. I stared at a yellow ring of urine on my sheets from someone else peeing the bed the night before. Nonetheless, I snuggled in, pulling my covers up, thankful the day was over.

As I lay on my back, the burning pain in my arms, back, and legs seemed to intensify. I tried to find comfort even amid the smell of urine. I tossed and turned, looking around at some of the empty beds near me. A slight distance away from me were other siblings in their beds already. Although they weren't close, I was thankful I would not be alone in the dark. I took a deep breath and sighed as I managed to roll over on my side to find the best position for comfort. The bright light still shone above for a few final minutes. I closed my eyes, and out of exhaustion and pain, soon slipped into a deep sleep.

CHAPTER THIRTY-NINE

I awoke in a panic, afraid morning had come. I could hear the voices of some of my siblings talking among one other. I popped my head up out of bed. I rubbed my eyes, trying to wake completely up and get my bearings before the staff made their way in. As my eyes began adjusting to the darkness, I blinked in disbelief at what I was seeing at the edge of my bed. A man in his late twenties or early thirties with long blond hair and a stern but smooth face sat within a golden halo. My body was in shock, and my mind rattled with self-doubt as I pondered whether this man was real or not.

I could hear the voices of some of my siblings talking amongst one another. Some could see the apparition, while others could not. My heart pounded within my chest as I stared at the man, in awe. Soon a familiar voice chimed in within the darkness. It was Luca. "Watch what I'm going to do," he whispered. I knew Luca was close as he talked, but since I could not see him I kept my eyes on the man who still stood near the edge of my bed. I was astonished this strange experience was real.

As I watched the spirit in front of me, nothing in his face or body movement changed. I was utterly shocked that others could see the same thing I could.

It gave me some relief to know I was not the only one who could see the man.

Sparks started to fly out of the left corner of my eye as I heard something collide with force, and within seconds a little light started to appear. I watched the light expand out of the corner of my eye. Luca's dark brown eye and light blue eye appeared within the glow of a flame that danced on top of a rock in his hand. The flame flickered gently, illuminating the scene, and I touched my arms to ensure that this was not a dream. The light flickered, revealing Jula on the left of me and Gage on my right.

Some of my other siblings asked what we were looking at, while the three of us stared at Luca in awe as he got closer to the entity. As I watched, he looked at the unknown thing with fierceness in its dark brown eyes. Then he placed the flame within the center of the apparition's body, making it disappear. *How could it be?* I wondered as Luca sat there without any fear. Then he pulled the light back to himself, revealing the spirit once more, in the same location.

A shiver of fear ran down my spine as I stared in awe, waiting for the otherworldly entity to fight back; it remained mute and unfazed. Curiosity about what had just taken place was overwhelming. That which I feared the most, Luca had faced. Out of desire to understand such a profound secret, I asked Luca if I could hold the rock. I took it, wondering at such a phenomenon in the physical realm. Jula and Gage sat silently beside me, both equally amazed.

How can this be? I wondered as I studied the rock in my hand. The base of it was ice cold while a flame danced ever so gently on its top. The rock was see-through and smooth, without wires or gimmicks attached. The longer I studied the rock, to try to understand its secrets, the more confused I became. Where had it come from?

Then it hit me. The rock I was holding in my hand was the same rock I had helped Luca collect in the alleyway.

CHAPTER FORTY

I knew where the rock had come from, so what was so special about it? I wondered this to myself as I placed my right hand over the flame, waving my fingers back and forth. I was trying to feel warmth, to justify the reality of this physical element, but there was no heat coming from its flame. I looked at Luca in disbelief, thinking my mind was playing tricks on me. I handed back the rock to Luca ever so gently, trying to convince myself that everything around me was only a dream. However, I knew that such a notion was a false presumption within my reality—that much was clear as I stared straight ahead at the spirit at the edge of my bed.

"Go ahead. Touch him. I dare you," Luca whispered, as the flame danced in front of him. I tried to process whether I had heard him correctly. When he repeated himself, I felt as if my chest had caved in. I could feel my heart's rhythm increasing out of terror, and I took a silent gulp, trying to not give away the fact that I was scared to death. Gage and Jula were both watching me.

I took in a deep breath and let out a sigh, trying to play it cool, to show I was not afraid, while I tossed my blanket back. The stink of urine that had been masked by my covers increased, times ten, it seemed.

I knew these were the least of my worries as I crawled slowly to the edge of my bed to face my biggest fear. My heart fluttered out of rhythm. I sat on my knees, at the edge of my bed, and looked the spirit up and down. I could see through him as his body hovered above the wooden floor.

I lifted my left hand in front of his face, waving it back and forth. Still I hesitated to touch him, thinking he was like a cobra that would soon strike. My hand's motion didn't even faze him as I looked into his brown eyes. I slowly placed my left hand inside his head, and I could see my hand within his aura. I was amazed as I twirled my hand inside his energy circumference while my siblings watched. As I twirled my hand, the vibration of the energy within the room elevated, and I could feel the hairs on the back of my neck rise. Quickly I pulled my hand back and hopped over the other side of my bed, grabbing my blanket so I could hide from the fury that might follow.

After a few moments of hiding, I mustered the courage to lower my blanket and peer over it. As I looked out, I noticed the spirit was still in the same spot, as if it had no jurisdiction within the realm of the physical. I was not sure if I could trust it or not, but the longer I watched the entity remain still, the more comfortable I became, lowering my blanket to my lap. I glanced at Luca again, in order to watch the flame dancing gracefully in his hand. I knew I could not fall back asleep. The light from the rock somehow brought me some solace as I watched the flame gyrating in the silence.

I started to become sleepy, and lay my head on my pillow, while trying to remain alert. For a long time I battled my weariness, fading in and out, in fear of missing out on something. I opened my eyes at intervals, fighting my exhaustion, but eventually Luca blew out the flame in his hand, bringing the room back into gloom. A little uneasiness came over me as the darkness settled back over us. The spirit remained near the edge of my bed. I knew I was not going to sleep tonight, out of fear that it was going to stay there through the night. Then, as I watched, it slowly faded away. I gazed in awe, trying to make sense of the spiritual wonder I'd just seen. My mind raced with all kind of different notions, but nothing made sense. Maybe it wasn't for me to understand. I lay there, gazing into the dark, afraid to fall asleep.

Soon exhaustion of mind and spirit prevailed. I closed my eyes and started to fall asleep. A sense of peace slowly started to move in, as if a holy hush had settled over me. Within seconds, I drifted into a deep and restorative sleep.

CHAPTER FORTY-ONE

I awoke to the sound of sticks banging on the edges of distant beds. I threw off my blanket, knowing that another day had arrived, and with it fear of punishment. The smell of urine from my bed filled the area. I quickly reached into my white underwear, to see if I had peed the bed during the night. As I felt around, a flutter of excitement came over me. I was in the clear.

I hopped out of bed before the staff made their way in and stood at the edge of my bed. Light flooded into our dark room, from the bedroom next door. I dreaded for the overhead lights to come on in our room as the cries and whimpering next door started to increase. The light coming in next to us cast shadows and within a second our light switch clicked on. The room soon flooded with the bright light from above, and I rubbed my eyes. I looked around to spot Jula, Gage, and Luca, to see if what I'd seen the night before was real.

As I looked around for them, a big female staff member with short brown hair made her way through the doorway, headed for me. I clenched my eyes out of fear, awaiting the inevitable pain. I felt her presence linger, but the pain never came. I opened my eyes, thinking I was in the clear, but she stood right in front of me. I could feel my heart beating faster as she grabbed me by the left arm and tugged me out of the bedroom, wearing only my underwear.

The woman dragged me through the other bedrooms and into the hallway. I wondered where I was going as we walked into the big white-and-yellow-tiled bathroom. I feared this was the secret place where they took children to get rid of them. I looked around at the empty bathroom and saw nothing except steam coming from a hot tub and a metal chair near the upper left side of the tub, covered with a big white sheet. The staff member released my arm and headed toward the tub, only to wave me closer. She ordered me to remove my underwear and get in. As I watched the steam build around me, a chill ran down my spine.

I placed my left foot in and then my right, doing as the staff asked. The water was hot, and in an instant it turned my skin red. As I sat in the tub that was normally crowded, and full of grime and feces, this time I wondered what was going to happen to me. I knew something was off and tried to make sense of it while I sat there, quietly listening to the water slosh around from my movements. The staff member armed herself with a bar of soap and a pink-handled nail brush.

CHAPTER FORTY-TWO

As the staff member made her way toward me with the soap, I looked again at the chair in the corner that was covered with a white sheet. I wondered what was so secretive about what lay underneath. Then suddenly it hit me: maybe some sort of tools were hidden under there, some implements of pain.

The chaperone grabbed my hand, bringing my attention back to her. She used the brush to clean above and under my nails. The pressure from the brush was overpoweringly painful, but I dared not pull away until she'd finished. I tried to keep my mind off the pain, but it was insistent. I felt my left knee grow inflamed while she scrubbed it with all her strength before switching to the other side. I held in my emotion, trying to keep calm as the water around me grew cloudy from filth. In reality, all I wanted to do was scream. However, I knew better than to do such a thing. The fear of any further punishment dominated my mind.

After she finished with my toes and rinsed me off, she ordered me to stand and get out of the tub and handed me a big towel. The yellow-tile floor was cold as I got out to dry off. Then I noticed that the chaperone was slowly making her way closer to the metal chair with the big white sheet covering it. My heart started throbbing underneath my breastbone. I thought of the stick or sharp tool that might wait for me as she yanked away the sheet.

I blinked and blinked again. I was incredulous! I simply could not believe my eyes! I stood there naked, staring at an apparently brand-new, thick, white and blue sweater that hung over the back of the chair. On the seat there were also a pair of new denim jeans, clean socks, and underwear stacked on top of them. There was even a pair of new white shoes on the side. I blinked a few more times, thinking I was dreaming and these things would disappear. I turned my attention to the staff member with a look of wonder and awe on my face.

"Put on the clothes," she said, as if reading my mind. I could barely contain my joy as I gladly accepted the challenge, heading over to the pile of fresh, clean clothes and grabbing the pair of new underwear that lay on top. The material was soft and appeared even brighter white up close, as I admired its newness before putting it on with excitement.

Next came my socks. They compressed around my feet with their softness as I reached for my jeans. The jeans were a little stiff, but I could feel the sturdiness of the denim as I slipped one foot in at a time. I could smell the aroma of strong dye as I pulled my new jeans up. I reached for my white undershirt next. It was spotless, with no stains, and I could feel the softness of the material against my skin. I slipped it on with joy, only to reach for my new sweater that lay on the back of the chair. The sweater was thick, and I held it up for a second, to admire its dark blue and pure white colors woven together. As I pulled it over my head, I took in a deep breath, letting the scent of pristine, freshly woven fabric fill my lungs.

CHAPTER FORTY-THREE

As I finished tying my shoes, the staff member's voice, echoing off the yellow tiles, instructed me to follow her. I felt as if I were walking on a soft cloud. My new shoes absorbed the impact with every stride as I walked down the stairs, listening to that familiar sound of the metal rods colliding with the inserts that held the rug in place. An exuberance I'd never felt before came over me as I followed the staff member in my new clothes—clothes that were not too small or too large and not old and frayed from hundreds of others wearing them out before me.

As I walked into the cafeteria, all my siblings ceased what they were doing and looked in my direction as I stood by the chaperone quietly, trying to make sense of what was happening. Another staff member's voice rang out, ordering all of us to get in line. In an instant chairs started scraping on the rigid concrete floor, and without hesitation I fell in line with everyone else who was being corralled forward. I was hungry and feared that punishment was soon upon us, as we made our way down the hallway, only to bank right toward the door that led outside.

I was not sure what was happening as the staff member opened the door and commanded us to only play near the entrance of the building. It was cloudy and slightly cold outside as I stood there dressed differently from everyone else, wondering why we were outside. Usually, we only played outside when the sun was out. I took it all in, nonetheless; I especially noticed an array of yellow, purple, and white pansies that bordered the paved path that led to the swing set. As I watched the flowers whispering in the breeze, I noticed the lanky chaperone was making his way toward the big green gate. I wondered why he was going that way, as laughter from my siblings behind me got my attention. I quickly turned around, and got a glimpse of Olga's red hair through the window as she walked down the long hallway.

CHAPTER FORTY-FOUR

Olga stood by the entrance of the building. She wore a scarf around her neck that made her eyes even more mesmerizing than usual. Her long, beautiful dark red hair complemented her features, I thought, as I watched her from a distance. Our eyes met, and she smiled at me, waving me over to come by her side as my other siblings gathered around. Her presence alone was enough to give me solace, and I ran to her. I could not resist her sweet, warm embrace. As I hugged her, a cold breeze swept through, intensifying the sweet aroma of Olga's perfume. I tried to articulate my words, to ask her why I was dressed differently, but as I stuttered, trying to utter a full sentence, she smiled and gently said, "I told you, Zoltan. You're going to America."

I couldn't believe my dreams were coming true. As I stared at Olga in disbelief, she pointed toward the big green gates while a white Dacia 1300 slowly started to make its way inside. My body was electrified with exultation as I stood there next to Olga.

The car parked. I could smell the fumes from the exhaust as I waited with anticipation to meet my new parents. The car shut off, and the back doors opened. A young lady with short blond hair and beautiful blue eyes stepped out of the white Dacia. Her expression was filled with exhaustion and bewilderment as I watched her take in the unfamiliar scene. Her piercing blue eyes danced as she looked at the tall scaffolds and the new construction that was underway. Another young lady soon stepped out of the vehicle behind her. She was thin, with a long torso, and her expression was stern. Even so, she had beautiful black hair that swirled in the wind as she started walking purposefully toward us. Her accent was thick.

Introducing herself as Elana the translator, she stepped forward to shake Olga's hand. She then turned around to let the young blond lady introduce herself. She seemed less intimidating to me as she stepped forward gracefully, introducing herself as Anna with a gentle voice. She shook Olga's hand; then her attention shifted down to me.

When our eyes met, I smiled at her, knowing it was the only gesture we both could readily understand.

CHAPTER FORTY-FIVE

Anna smiled back at me, pulling out her camera, waving it back and forth as she said something in English that sounded like gibberish to me. Olga looked at me with enthusiasm and told me to grab a couple of my friends and head to her office for some pictures. I scanned the perimeter, hesitant, as an overwhelming joy rushed through me. I grabbed the two closest people as Olga ushered the rest of the guests inside. In order to not miss out on anything, I followed right behind them, with Gage and Florin next to me.

As I walked down the long hallway, my siblings from outside crowded the windows, watching our every move. While Olga, Anna, and Elana chatted back and forth along the way, I dreamed about what America would be like. Soon we turned into Olga's office, and my siblings outside were out of sight. The smell of Olga's sweet perfume engulfed me as I entered the office. I could not get enough, taking in another big breath as I made my way toward the black leather couch.

Gage and Florin followed my lead as Olga closed the office door behind us. The office was small but cozy, and I could feel myself sinking into the couch as I watched Anna pulling out her black and yellow disposable camera again. I didn't want to move, because the couch was so comfortable, but I propped myself up so I wouldn't disappoint anyone, and wrapped my arms around Gage and Florin. Anna pointed the camera at us, said "Cheese," and pressed the button. A bright flash went off and I sat blinking, amazed at such a bright light. Anna smiled joyfully while winding the film in her camera.

Olga spoke up, calling Anna's name in a gentle manner, and ushered her to sit across from her desk as she walked behind it to grab a pile of paperwork. I let my arms come to a rest as I leaned back into the black leather couch. Trying to understand what was happening, I tuned into the facial expressions and the sounds that were around me.

A brief silence settled over the room, and I tried to make sense of it. The only thing I could see was Olga's finger pointing to the paper. The only thing I could hear was the pen's scratching as a signature appeared on every page. The ruffling of the paperwork soon came to a halt, and I watched intently as Olga grabbed the paperwork, tapping her desk with a big smile on her face.

"Go outside," she said. "Take a few more pictures."

CHAPTER FORTY-SIX

Though the sky was cloudy and gray, and the wind a little cold, my siblings smiled gleefully at the camera. Anna yelled, "Cheese," with a big smile on her face. Everyone gathered around me and Olga, with the colorful pansies dancing in the background. I blinked as the flash caught me by surprise again. All around me was the roar of excitement and laughter from my siblings. Joy filled the air as Anna said, "Thank you," and lowered her camera.

Soon Olga shooed us away to go and play, and without thinking twice about it I took off in my new shoes. I felt as if I were on a cloud, running around, bobbing and weaving between my siblings while exhilaration pumped through me. However, eventually out of exhaustion, I came to a halt. I could feel my heart hammer in my chest as I gazed around my environment. As I admired my surroundings, I wished for the day to never end. I watched some of my siblings play tag, while others gathered around Olga, near the pansies. There was joy in all of my siblings.

I looked at Anna. She was taking pictures of the orphanage, with Elana. As they made their way back to the car, I wondered to myself if they knew they had set us free. It amazed me, how they could pause time and bring out the best in everyone. Within just a couple of hours, they had made a memory that would last my siblings and me for a lifetime.

While I took it all in, a voice from behind startled me, making me turn around quickly. I paused, amazed, as I stared into the blue eyes of the big-headed kid. His demeanor was kind and gentle. I looked into his innocent, beautiful blue eyes, and he pointed to his big forehead where a big scar remained, before he quickly took off.

CHAPTER FORTY-SEVEN

My attention settled back on Anna. I could see her lowering the camera, saying goodbye to my siblings, as she started making her way back to the driveway. Panic rose in me while I watched Olga join her. They made their way to the Dacia. I kept repeating Olga's words in my head: "You are going to America." I knew my dreams were often nothing more than my imagination as I watched Elana get in the car first. I knew I needed to face reality and get ready for the worst.

Both women came to a stop in front of the white Dacia, and I repeated to myself, "I am going to America," even as the back car door was already swung wide open for Anna to get in for a quick getaway. I wanted to believe that I was going to America, but as I said Olga's words, over and over, doubt continued to creep in.

Olga called my name and made eye contact with me. I quickly ran toward her with excitement as she held her arms wide open. My doubt of her promise faded as she embraced me. I smelled her sweet perfume; I could feel her sorrow as well as her joy as she said goodbye to me and let me go.

"You're going to America. Anna is going to be your new mom," she told me. I could not believe my dreams were actually coming true that day, in that hour. Olga looked me in the eyes for the last time before ushering me into the car.

While my siblings surrounded the vehicle, and I made my way inside, the gas fumes filled my lungs. I gazed around at the red and black car seats, then I scooted over to the far-right side of the seat, feeling overwhelmed and unsure about what would happen to me next.

Anna entered the vehicle, waving her final goodbye before closing the back car door. As I sat there, the feeling of not wanting to leave came over me. I knew the terror my life there had brought, but I also feared leaving everything I had always known. I wondered if this was what it felt like for all the other kids who had been adopted, when they were on the other side of the car window.

I looked at my siblings as we started to move forward. I could feel my stomach shift within me, and my emotions started to push toward the surface. I knew I needed to be strong, as my dreams started to come to fruition, yet the further away I got from the only place I had ever known as my home, the weaker I became. I turned around in my seat, looking through the back window, watching my home slowly fade into the background as my siblings chased the car, as if it were their dream they were running after.

While we passed through the big green gate to turn right, my emotions got the best of me, and tears streamed from my eyes. I knew I needed to stop crying, but the further away I got from everything that was familiar to me, the louder I cried. An array of emotions poured out of me. Anna pulled out a hoagie sandwich to quiet me, but the only thing I could do was shake my head side to side and say, “No.” Tears drenched my sweater, and I became weak and tired. I tried to resist sleep, but as I dozed, I placed my head on Anna’s lap and drifted off to dream in the arms of my angel . . .

AFTERWORD

Thank you for taking the time to read and thereby share my journey. Perhaps one of the most important things I have learned along the way is that hurt, pain, and fear are everywhere. They have no titles, know no boundaries. No one can outgrow their cycle, no matter how rich, poor, or educated one becomes. However, within my trials and tribulations, along my journey, I also encountered mercy, kindness, wisdom, and opportunities that allowed my deepest dreams to come true through the most genuine gestures of human kindness.

I wrote this story not seeking pity, but in hopes of enlightening those who read my story to see the blessing that can take place through just the simple acts of kindness, patience, and love. If we act with love, kindness, and hope—no strings attached—we can create a collateral beauty in life among the chaos. Simply put, we can change someone's day—and someone's life—with a simple split-second gesture of love or gentle act of kindness.

For me, as with each of us, one story begins where another ends.

I was nine years of age when I was adopted from that Romanian orphanage and brought to America. I am thankful for those parents who took a leap of faith and adopted me. My adoption experience was not without its challenges. Yet, for my parents—and for my siblings—I will always be grateful.

The important fact is this: From that abandoned, beaten, and abused little boy in Romania, to today, when I am a productive member of American society, with a college education and viable employment, my steps have been ordered by a God who is great and gracious to us all. I am waiting to see what the rest of the story He is writing with my life will be.

"Yesterday is history, tomorrow is a mystery, but today is a gift . . . that is why it is called the present."

(Master Oogway in Dreamworks Animation's Kung Fu Panda)

Mission Statement: To inspire people worldwide to discover their true worth and values regardless of their background or upbringing.

Vision Statement: To see a world empowered by those from all walks of life living out of love, instead of greed.

ABOUT THE AUTHOR

ZOLTAN POWELL is a graduate of Miami Oxford University. He holds a Bachelor's Degree in Integrative Studies with a concentration in Personal Health Perspectives and Business Management, with a minor in Criminology. He also holds an Associate's Degree in Business Management and Technology. He enjoys sharing time with friends and family. In his spare time he loves to travel, write, and stay active while inspiring others all along the way.

TO CONTACT THE AUTHOR FOR SPEAKING ENGAGEMENTS: tabularasaimmersion@gmail.com

Made in the USA
Monee, IL
12 August 2020

38061712R00105